-The
Mathematical
Sciences: -
A Report

BY THE
COMMITTEE ON SUPPORT OF RESEARCH IN THE
MATHEMATICAL SCIENCES
OF THE
NATIONAL RESEARCH COUNCIL
FOR THE
COMMITTEE ON SCIENCE AND PUBLIC POLICY
NATIONAL ACADEMY OF SCIENCES

PUBLICATION 1681

National Academy of Sciences
WASHINGTON, D.C.
1968

Available from

Printing and Publishing Office
National Academy of Sciences
2101 Constitution Avenue
Washington, D.C. 20418

Library of Congress Catalog Card Number 68–61402

First printing, November 1968
Second printing, April 1969

Dr. Frederick Seitz, President
National Academy of Sciences
2101 Constitution Avenue
Washington, D.C. 20418

Dear Dr. Seitz:

The Committee on Science and Public Policy takes pleasure in forwarding to you the report of the Committee on Support of Research in the Mathematical Sciences. Our committee has reviewed this report at several stages in its development, and we feel that it presents a clear and cogent case for the support of the mathematical sciences and a good picture of the present state of both research and education in mathematics and related disciplines. The extraordinary rate at which classical mathematical theorems have fallen before the onslaught of young American mathematicians in recent years is impressive, as is the leading position acquired by the United States in recent times.

The report calls attention to the penetration of mathematics and mathematical modes of thought into many new areas of scholarship and the resultant great increase in the relative enrollment in undergraduate mathematics courses, especially at the upper levels. It also brings out the increasing importance of mathematical methods in industry and government, the rapid growth in employment of mathematical scientists outside the universities, and the pace of growth of mathematical sciences relative to that of all other disciplines.

The report calls attention to the special problem of computer science in universities, brought about by its high cost relative to the rest of mathematical research and education and by the fact that it is both a scientific and an engineering discipline, which has made it difficult to fit into the academic structure. Meaningful research in computer science often requires rather large-scale support for complex projects of a partly developmental nature that do not always lend themselves to the project-grant type of support typical in pure mathematics and some other scientific disciplines. The development of computer science only as a *by-product of the application of computer techniques in other fields often results in failure to develop a distinctive body of theory and technique in computer science in its own right.*

The report identifies special problems concerning mathematical statistics and physical (i.e., classical applied) mathematics. In physical mathematics the problem is not the need for rapid growth of financial support, as in computer science, but for a place in the academic structure that does not tie it too closely to a particular set of applications. The authors of this report feel that there are too few distinguished applied-mathematics groups in American universities, and that special encouragement is needed for building such groups. Whatever place applied mathematical sciences find in the academic structure, however, it is essential to maintain a strong and continuing interaction between these sciences and pure mathematics—an interaction in which ideas and people must move in both directions.

An outstanding feature of this report in comparison with some of the earlier disciplinary reports is the attention it devotes to questions of education, not only for mathematical scientists but also for the many users of mathematics.

The Committee on Support of Research in Mathematical Sciences is to be congratulated not only for its impressive work in the preparation of the present volume but also for the valuable contributions of two supplementary volumes produced under its aegis. One of these, the detailed report of the Committee's Panel on Undergraduate Education, analyzes the uniquely demanding special problems of American undergraduate education in the mathematical sciences and makes many suggestions for dealing with these problems. The other, a collection of twenty-two essays by distinguished mathematical scientists, brings together, in a form accessible to a wide range of readers, expositions of the achievements, traditions, and prospects in a rich variety of mathematical fields.

Sincerely,

HARVEY BROOKS, *Chairman*
Committee on Science and Public Policy

iv

THIS REPORT on the mathematical sciences is another in the series of comprehensive survey reports on major fields of science prepared under the aegis of the Academy's Committee on Science and Public Policy.

With the growing importance of the mathematical sciences, both in their own right and through their penetration of other sciences and of technology, it has become clear that a report on mathematics should be added to the survey reports. Thus the Committee on Support of Research in the Mathematical Sciences was appointed to undertake the preparation of such a report under the chairmanship of Professor Lipman Bers.

I am pleased to express gratitude to the Committee for its dedicated work. I trust the findings and recommendations set forth here will prove useful to those with responsibilities in the continuing support of American science.

FREDERICK SEITZ, President
National Academy of Sciences

Committee on Science and Public Policy

Committee on Support of Research in the Mathematical Sciences

Foreword

The Committee on Support of Research in the Mathematical Sciences (COSRIMS) was appointed by the Division of Mathematical Sciences of the National Research Council at the instigation of the Committee on Science and Public Policy of the National Academy of Sciences. Our task was to assess the present status and the projected future needs, especially fiscal needs, of the mathematical sciences. It was clear to us from the very beginning of our work that our report would have to differ somewhat in structure from the corresponding reports for other disciplines that had already appeared.

Though mathematics provides the common language for all sciences, we realize that even scientific readers of our report, let alone nonscientists, may feel that they are not adequately informed about what mathematical research, especially modern mathematical research, consists of. Similarly, even professional mathematicians, or scientists who customarily use mathematics in their work, may be unaware of the manifold applications of mathematics in various sciences and technologies, especially the new applications influenced by the computer revolution.

To provide additional background of factual information concerning the mathematical sciences, we are supplementing our report with a collection of essays, written by distinguished authors on various topics in mathematics, in the applied mathematical sciences, and in the applications of mathematics. With three exceptions, which are reprints, these essays were written expressly for this collection. They are intended not only for the nonmathematical scientist but also for the scientifically oriented layman.

Mathematics pervades our whole educational system. As a matter of fact, we believe that the mathematical community has no obligations more important than those concerned with education, the most critical area being collegiate education. We have, therefore, included in our report questions of policy regarding higher education. Our Panel on Undergraduate Education has carried out an intensive study of this area; its report is presented in a separate volume of our report.

Simultaneously with our activities, the Conference Board of the Mathematical Sciences has been carrying out a survey of research and education in mathematics, and its Survey Committee has agreed to act as a fact-finding agency for our Committee. The Conference Board Survey Committee's report will contain a wealth of factual and statistical material pertaining to the matters discussed in our report. We take this opportunity to express our gratitude to the Survey Committee and to the Ford Foundation which supported their work.

The activities of our Committee have been financed mainly by a grant from the National Science Foundation. This has been supplemented by smaller grants from the Sloan Foundation, the Conference Board of the Mathematical Sciences, the American Mathematical Society, the Association for Computing Machinery, the Association for Symbolic Logic, the Institute of Mathematical Statistics, the Mathematical Association of America, the National Council of Teachers of Mathematics, the Operations Research Society of America, and the Society for Industrial and Applied Mathematics. Columbia University has generously provided us with office space and many auxiliary services. To all these organizations we express our thanks.

We are deeply indebted to the authors of the essays, to the chairmen and members of our panels, and to the many other individuals who have contributed their time and expertise to our undertaking.

January 20, 1968   LIPMAN BERS
Chairman, Committee on Support
of Research in the
Mathematical Sciences

Contents

I SUMMARY

1 MATHEMATICS AND SOCIETY 3

The Mathematization of Culture 3
The Need for Mathematically Trained People 5
Applied Mathematical Sciences 6
Core Mathematics 8
The Position of the United States in Mathematics 10

2 RECOMMENDATIONS 13

Research 15
Education 24
Surveys and Studies 31
Implications for Program and Resources Planning 32

II THE STATE OF THE MATHEMATICAL SCIENCES

3 THE COMMUNITY OF MATHEMATICS 45

Historical Perspectives 45
The Nature of Mathematics 48
Core and Applications 51
Criticisms and Tensions 53
Improving Communications 55

4   CORE MATHEMATICS   57

Mathematical Logic   57
Number Theory   60
Combinatorial Analysis   62
Algebra   62
Analysis   68
Geometry   77

5   APPLIED MATHEMATICAL SCIENCES   84

Fluid Dynamics: An Example of Physical Mathematics   85
Statistics   88
Computer Science   92
Optimized Allocation, Control, and Decisions   97
Other Areas   99

6   EXAMPLES OF MATHEMATICS IN USE   101

Mathematics and Physics   102
Mathematical Sciences in Engineering   104
An Example from the Environmental Sciences: Numerical
   Weather Prediction   108
Mathematical Sciences in Economics   110
Mathematics in Finance and Insurance   111
Mathematics in Management and Operations   113
Concluding Remarks   114

III   THE MATHEMATICAL SCIENCES IN EDUCATION

7   UNDERGRADUATE EDUCATION   121

The Increase in Mathematics Majors   122
Total Enrollments in the Mathematical Sciences   124
Quality and Distribution of Mathematical-Science
   Faculty   127
The Junior Colleges   130
The Mathematics Faculty in Junior Colleges   133

8   GRADUATE EDUCATION   135

    The Master's Degree   136
    The Doctorate in the Mathematical Sciences   138
    The Doctorate of Philosophy and Intermediate Degrees   141
    Graduate-Student Participation in Undergraduate
      Teaching   145

9   SPECIAL EDUCATIONAL ISSUES   147

    The College Teacher   147
    Applied Mathematics   149
    Computer Science   152
    Statistics   156
    Research versus Teaching   158
    Wasted Mathematical Talent   159

IV   LEVEL AND FORMS OF SUPPORT

10   FEDERAL SUPPORT OF RESEARCH   163

    Level and Sources of Support   163
    The Role of the Mission-Oriented Agencies   167
    Forms of Support   170
    Time and Effort Reporting   177

11   FEDERAL SUPPORT OF EDUCATION   179

    Graduate Education   179
    Postdoctoral Research Education   182
    Continuing Education for College Teachers   184

12   PRIVATE FOUNDATIONS   187

    Grants by Private Foundations   187
    Comments   188

13   INDUSTRIAL AND GOVERNMENT LABORATORIES   190

    Activities at Some Major Laboratories   191
    The General Situation and Its Problems   192
    Comments   193

V CONCLUSIONS

14 TASKS AND NEEDS 197

The Core 197
Physical Mathematics 201
Statistics 203
Computer Science 205
Operations Research and Management Science 207
Other Areas 208

15 THE MATHEMATICAL SCIENCES IN SOCIETY'S SERVICE 211

The Mathematical Population 211
Mathematical Strategy 214
Transfer Times 215
Emergencies 217
The Level of Investment 217
Growth Cannot Be Forever 218
The Nonutilitarian View 220

REFERENCES 221

APPENDIXES

APPENDIX A 227

Individuals Who Contributed to the Work of COSRIMS

APPENDIX B 233

Final Report of the American Mathematical Society's Committee
on Information Exchange and Publication in Mathematics

APPENDIX C 243

The Role of the Private Foundations in the Support of
Mathematics

APPENDIX D 249

The Support of Computer Use in Higher Education

APPENDIX E 253

PhD Origins of Mathematicians in Certain Categories

I

Summary

1

Mathematics and Society

The recent history of mathematics has been like that of science generally. The number of investigators has grown rapidly and so have the pace and quality of the research. An intellectual leadership that used to reside in Western Europe is now shared by Americans and others.

Today, society, especially through other sciences and technologies, makes unprecedented demands on mathematics and on the community of mathematical scientists. The purpose of this report is to identify the major demands, to assess the capabilities of the mathematical community to satisfy them, and to propose measures for preserving and extending these capabilities.

THE MATHEMATIZATION OF CULTURE

Mathematics has long played a central role in the intellectual and technological history of mankind. Yet this statement hardly begins to convey or account for the current explosive penetration of mathematical methods into other disciplines, amounting to a virtual "mathematization of culture."

Mathematics can be described as the art of symbolic reasoning. Mathematics is present wherever chains of manipulations of abstract symbols are used; such chains may occur in the mind of a human being, as marks on paper, or in an electronic computer. Symbolic reasoning appears to have been first used in connection with counting. For this reason, mathematics is sometimes described,

3

though not completely accurately, as the science of numbers. In fact, it turns out that all symbolic reasoning may be reduced to manipulation of whole numbers; and it is this fact that makes the digital computer into the universal tool it is.

Mathematics as we know it originated more than 2,000 years ago with the Greeks. They transformed into a deductive science the collection of facts and procedures about numbers and geometric figures known to the older civilizations of Egypt and Babylon. The Greeks applied mathematics only to astronomy and statics. The possibility of applying it to other sciences, in particular to dynamics, was discovered in the sixteenth and seventeenth centuries. This discovery revolutionized mathematics; it led to the creation of calculus and thereby made modern physical science and technology possible.

The development of the physical sciences continues to use mathematical techniques and concepts. So do the new technologies based on the discoveries of the physical sciences. Furthermore, these sciences and technologies use mathematical techniques of ever-increasing sophistication, so that the mounting role of physical sciences and technologies in the contemporary world is a dominant aspect of the mathematization of culture. It is, however, not the only aspect. Mathematical methods are penetrating into fields of knowledge that have been essentially shielded from mathematics until not long ago; for instance, the life sciences. The twentieth-century penetration of mathematical methods into the biological sciences has come about in several ways, perhaps most importantly through the increasing study of biological phenomena by the methods of chemical physics. The development of statistics, which the needs of the biological sciences helped to stimulate, has led to the extensive field of biostatistics. This has connections with mathematical genetics, which has evolved out of the celebrated Mendelian laws of inheritance, and with mathematical ecology, which is concerned with such interactions as competition for food or the feeding of one species on another. Differential-equation models for the conduction of signals along nerve fibers have had notable success. Computer simulation of functions of living organisms is just one of the ways in which computers are becoming increasingly important in the biological sciences.

Mathematics is penetrating the social and behavioral sciences, too, and even traditionally humanistic areas. Mathematical economics is now a central part of economics. The field of econometrics has grown out of applications of probability and statistics in economics; and statistical techniques are important in anthropology, sociology, political science, and psychology. Analysis of mathematical models for various social phenomena has been greatly aided by computer simulation and data processing. The mathematical viewpoint has even found new application in linguistics.

The above remarks refer to the mathematization of various academic disciplines. Mathematics is also becoming an indispensable tool in the world of government, industry, and business. The terms "operations research" and "management science" are among those describing the rapidly growing use of mathematical methods to solve problems which arise in managing complicated systems involving the movement and allocation of goods and services.

Computers have extended the possibility of applying mathematical methods to a degree that would have seemed fantastic a short time ago. Computer science, which deals with manifold problems of building and utilizing computers, contains, among other things, very important mathematical components.

THE NEED FOR MATHEMATICALLY TRAINED PEOPLE

The mathematization of our society brings with it an increasing need for people able to understand and use mathematics. This need manifests itself at various levels.

We need people who can teach mathematics in grade school in a way that will not create a permanent psychological block against mathematics in so many of our fellow citizens. We need people who can understand a simple formula, read a graph, interpret a statement about probability. Indeed, all citizens should have these skills. We need people who are able to teach mathematics in high school and cope with the necessarily changing curriculum. We need people who know what computers can do, and also what they cannot do. We need computer programmers who can work with understanding and efficiency. We need engineers, physicists, chemists, geologists, astronomers, biologists, physicians, economists, sociologists, and psychologists who possess the mathematical tools used today in their respective disciplines and who have the mathematical literacy for learning the new skills that will be needed tomorrow. Equally we need, though in smaller numbers of course, people in these fields who are able to use mathematical tools creatively and if necessary to modify existing mathematical methods. The numbers are hard to estimate, but it is clear that our society needs many more mathematically literate and educated people than are available now. For instance, computer programmers are already more numerous than high school teachers of mathematics, and their numbers will continue to increase.

These demands call for massive amounts of mathematical education at all levels and so produce a mounting pressure on the mathematical community. To do all this training calls for a larger body of mathematics teachers. It is difficult to expand the supply rapidly enough. Since teachers of intermediate-level mathematics must themselves be trained by people of higher competence, these pressures also quickly transmit themselves to the relatively small community of mathematical scientists who do research. Many of the needs of mathematics for support come from a need for balanced growth meeting all these requirements.

Since we recognize a rising level of mathematical literacy as a national objective, and since the community of mathematical scientists bears the primary responsibility for attaining this objective, our report cannot separate problems of research from problems of education, including those of undergraduate education. (See both Part III and the report[1],* of our Panel on Undergraduate Education.)

Applied Mathematical Sciences

There are now four major areas in the mathematical sciences that have particularly direct and important relationships with other sciences and technologies: computer science, operations research, statistics, and physical mathematics (classical applied mathematics). We shall ordinarily refer to these as *applied mathematical sciences*. For statistics and computer science there is a more accurate term, *partly mathematical sciences,* which we shall sometimes use in recognition of the individual character of these fields and their strong extramathematical components.

These four major areas must each have special attention if we are to come close to meeting national needs. At the same time, there is a need for general support of applied mathematical sciences in a way, not closely tied to particular applications, that will encour-

* Superscript numbers refer to the list of references at the end of the report.

age creative interaction between mathematics, science, and technology, and among the various applied mathematical sciences themselves.

The sciences and technologies associated with the computer—whether concerned with the nature of information and language, the simulation of cognitive processes, the computer programs that bring individual problems of all kinds to today's computing systems, the software programs that convert cold hardware into a complex computing system, or the hardware itself—face an intense and growing challenge.

The field sometimes labeled operations research is now growing rapidly, though not so explosively as computer science. Its emphasis today is on solving problems of allocation (routing problems and scheduling problems are two major types) and on a broad class of operational applications of probability (inventory management and improving the service of queues and waiting lines, for example). Again there are national needs both for a substantial body of people who can apply the techniques effectively and for a leadership that can innovate, reshape, and transform.

The field of statistics and data analysis is older and more firmly established than the two just described. Yet there is still a shortage of statisticians who can bring mathematical techniques and insights to diverse applications. The development of computer techniques is also having a strong impact on this field.

Physical mathematics, also called classical applied mathematics, has evolved into various modern forms. In its traditional form, it emphasized the mathematics essential to classical physics and the established fields of engineering. Even more it emphasized the evolution of the mathematical models under study. Nowadays, the concepts of physics have been expanded to include the well-established aspects of quantum mechanics and the theory of relativity. New developments apply to an ever greater variety of subject-matter fields, and we must now look once again toward a closer collaboration and mutual stimulation between mathematics and all the other sciences.

Alongside the four main applied mathematical sciences there are still newer areas of application where no self-identifying community of mathematical scientists yet exists—areas of central importance to a variety of national objectives of great and growing concern. The interplay between mathematics and sciences and the mutual stimulation, cooperation, and transfer of ideas among applied mathematicians working in diverse areas all suggest that the applied mathematical sciences, because of their common features, constitute an area of study worthy of support in its own right.

CORE MATHEMATICS

The foundation of the manifold mathematical activities just discussed is the central core of mathematics—the traditional disciplines of logic, number theory, algebra, geometry, and analysis that have been the domains of the so-called "pure mathematician." The relationship between the core and applied areas is not one-sided; many of the essential ideas and concepts in the central core can be traced ultimately to problems arising outside of mathematics itself. In the central core, mathematical ideas and techniques, no matter what their origin, are analyzed, generalized, codified, and transformed into tools of wide applicability.

In assessing the importance of the core, one should keep in mind that there is always an interplay and exchange of ideas between so-called "pure" mathematics, that is, mathematics pursued primarily for intrinsic intellectual and aesthetic reasons, and so-called "applied" mathematics, that is, mathematics consciously used as a tool for understanding various aspects of nature.

Thus geometry, literally "earth measurement," originated as an applied art, presumably in the Nile delta. The Greeks transformed it into a pure deductive science, the prototype of pure mathematics. Among the geometric objects studied by the Greeks were the curves (ellipses, parabolas, hyperbolas) obtained by intersecting a cone with a plane. These "conic sections," though they may have been discovered by observing sundials, were then of interest to the pure mathematicians alone. Today conic sections are working tools of engineers, physicists, and astronomers. On the other hand, calculus, which was developed by Newton as a mathematical tool for studying the motions of physical bodies, is also the foundation of a large part of modern "pure" mathematics.

The most spectacular uses of core mathematics are its direct applications in science and technology. Remarkably enough, it is impossible to predict which parts of mathematics will turn out to be important in other fields. We have one guide: Widely useful mathematics, for the most part, has proved to be also the kind that mathematicians earlier characterized as "profound" or "beautiful."

Important mathematical ideas have also been generated by people who were not professional mathematicians.

The time lag of 2,000 years between the invention of the conic sections and their applications in astronomy is, of course, not typical of recent developments. But the unexpected character of the application is typical. The theory of Lie groups, for instance, was developed for many years because of its intrinsic mathematical interest. It seems now to be the natural way of describing symmetries in elementary-particle physics. The theory of analytic functions of several complex variables has been undergoing a dramatic development during the last two decades. The experts in this theory were quite surprised to discover its usefulness in quantum field theory.

We stress once more the totally unpredictable nature of such applications. It is not the motivation of the mathematician who creates a new theory that determines its future relevance to other fields of knowledge. In particular, one should not be repelled by the seemingly frivolous origins of many mathematical theories. A puzzle about the seven bridges in Königsberg led to the theory of graphs, a basic mathematical tool of computer science, and indirectly influenced the development of topology. A question raised by a professional gambler led Pascal and Fermat to the theory of probability.

But the application of a particular mathematical result or a specific mathematical concept is not the only way in which core mathematics is used. The total impact of mathematics on science and technology is more difficult to document but probably even more important. In all such applications of mathematics (model building and mathematical reasoning about models, statistical analysis, the use of computers), the investigators will use some of the concepts, methods, and results developed by core mathematicians. In a typical case, however, they will not find in the storehouse of core mathematics the precise tools they need but will rather have to develop those tools either alone or in cooperation with mathematicians. How successful they will be depends to a large extent on the general status of mathematics in the country, on the level of mathematical knowledge among the people involved, and on the number and quality of mathematically trained people.

All this depends ultimately on a healthy and vigorous development within the central core of mathematics. We are convinced that without this one cannot have efficient use of mathematical methods in science and technology, imaginative mathematization of new fields, or spirited and effective teaching of mathematics at all levels.

The central core of mathematics is not static. It is now undergoing rapid and in many ways revolutionary development. Many old and famous problems are being solved. The traditional boundaries between different mathematical subfields are disappearing. New unifying ideas are applied with great success. Though dynamic, the central core of mathematics preserves historical continuity and uncompromisingly high standards.

THE POSITION OF THE UNITED STATES IN MATHEMATICS

At the beginning of this century, mathematical research activity in this country was chiefly concentrated in a very few centers. Noteworthy was the center at The University of Chicago under the leadership of E. H. Moore, himself trained in Europe. Among Moore's illustrious students were Oswald Veblen, G. D. Birkhoff, and Leonard Dickson, each a major figure in mathematics. In the interval between World Wars I and II, mathematics in the United States became somewhat more important relative to world mathematics.

Political developments in Europe in the 1930's led many European mathematicians to seek refuge in the United States and to become active members of the American mathematical community. This greatly stimulated mathematical research activity in this country. The Institute for Advanced Study in Princeton became a world center of mathematical research. Until after the Second World War, however, financial support for mathematical activity was extremely limited, and only a handful of undergraduates seriously considered careers in research mathematics.

During World War II, the relevance of mathematics to the technological might of the nation and the critical shortage of mathematically trained people became apparent. After the war, the mathematical sciences became for the first time a concern of the federal government, initially through the research departments of defense agencies and then also through the National Science Foundation. While the influx of federal money into the support of mathematics was very modest compared with the funds poured into such expensive fields as high-energy physics, its effect on the scientific life of the United States was stupendous.

Before World War II, the United States was a consumer of mathematics and mathematical talent. Now the United States is universally recognized as the leading producer of these. Moreover, graduate education in mathematical sciences at major centers in this country is far superior to that in all but two or three centers in the rest of the world. Some more specific indicators of the position of the United States in the mathematical world are given below.

1. International congresses of mathematicians, meeting at roughly four-year intervals, were inaugurated around the turn of the century. The earliest such congress, in 1897 in Zurich, was attended by only about 200, whereas at the most recent congress in 1966 in Moscow, attendance was approximately 4,300. An invitation to a mathematician to address an international congress evidences worldwide recognition of his contributions to mathematical discovery at the very highest level.

During the first four international congresses, those of 1897, 1900, 1904, and 1908, there were 26 invited addresses, of which only one was by an American.* During the four most recent congresses, those of 1954, 1958, 1962, and 1966, there were 274 invited addresses, of which 96, more than one third, were by U.S. mathematicians.

2. The Fields Medals, for recognition of distinguished achievement by younger mathematicians anywhere in the world, were established in 1932 by the late Professor J. C. Fields. Beginning with the Oslo congress of 1936, two Fields Medals have been awarded at each international congress of mathematicians, except that most recently at the Moscow congress of 1966 four were awarded. In all, 14 Fields Medals have been awarded, with the distribution of medalists by country as follows: France, four; the United States, four; England, two; Finland, Japan, Norway, and Sweden, one each.

Of the 12 Fields Medalists since 1945, three have been Americans trained in America: Paul Cohen (1966), John Milnor (1962), and Stephen Smale (1966). Three others are long-time residents of the

---

* Simon Newcomb, who addressed the 1908 congress in Rome on the history and present status of the theory of lunar motion. Participants at this congress numbered 535, of whom 16 were from the United States.

United States and should now be considered to be members of the U.S. mathematical community. Four or five others have been and are frequent visitors to the United States, each having spent at least one academic year here. Some of these are active collaborators with various American mathematicians.

3. English has recently become the dominant language in world mathematical circles. For instance, in the German journal, *Mathematische Annalen,* the percentage of papers in English rose from approximately 5 percent in the mid-1930's to nearly 20 percent in the mid-1950's, and to 55 percent in the mid-1960's.

4. In some representative issues of three of the leading mathematical journals of Europe, *Acta Mathematica* (Sweden), *Commentarii Mathematici Helvetici* (Switzerland), and *Mathematische Annalen* (Germany), the following percentages of references to papers in U.S. journals were found:

YEAR	*Acta* *Math.*	*Comment.* *Math. Helv.*	*Math.* *Ann.*
1935	3%	12%	4%
1950	12%	24%	4%
1965	42%	25%	25%

5. There has been a significant increase in the number of foreign mathematicians visiting in this country. Figures assembled by the American Mathematical Society show that, in 1956, 73 foreign mathematicians spent at least a semester at a U.S. university; in 1960, the number came to 144; in 1965 there were 199 such visitors. In addition, other foreign mathematicians made briefer or more casual visits or more lengthy stays outside universities.

2

Recommendations

Our recommendations aim at enabling the community of mathematical sciences to do all it can toward meeting national needs. Even if all these recommendations are implemented, inherent limitations on the rate of growth of research and teaching activities in the mathematical sciences will make it impossible to meet all these needs fully. It is therefore necessary to move as vigorously as possible toward the recommended goals.*

The needs, outlined in the preceding chapter and throughout our report, are an inevitable consequence of the growing complexity of our society and its increasing dependence on a variety of science-based technologies. These technologies, and the physical, biological, and behavioral sciences that support them, are becoming more and more mathematized. They utilize the ideas and techniques of core mathematics and the methods and results of physical mathematics, statistics, and other applied mathematical sciences. Most of these technologies depend, often in a crucial way, on effective use of electronic computers. Accordingly, society needs a rising level of mathematical literacy and competence at all levels, a sufficient supply of mathematically trained people in many sciences and professions, and a sufficient number of qualified mathematical scientists.

* *Added in proof:* All our estimates and predictions about future numbers of PhD's were formulated before the February 1968 issuance of new Selective Service rules affecting graduate students. If these rules should result in a serious depletion of the graduate student population, this would, of course, intensify the predicted shortage of PhD's in the mathematical sciences.

13

Research in the mathematical sciences serves a twofold social function. The research workers create, develop, refine, and adapt the mathematical tools needed now and in the future for the manifold applications of mathematics and for the growth of the mathematical sciences themselves. The same people, because of the insight and stimulation acquired through active participation in research, are the leaders of the whole educational effort of the mathematical community. A thoughtful policy concerning support of research has to be responsive to both aspects.

In these recommendations, as in the report as a whole, we have treated research and education together. Research apprenticeship, as carried out by postdoctoral fellows and research instructors and by graduate students writing theses, is inseparable from research. Education at the undergraduate and early graduate levels is so intimately related—on a long time scale—to research, that to consider the continuing good of one without the other would be foolish. From a national point of view, these are parts of one problem, a problem that must be faced in its entirety.

Our recommendations, to be stated and discussed below, fall under six main heads:

Improvement in the quality of education in the mathematical sciences at the undergraduate level through expanded federal support, especially at key points. There is a growing shortage of college teachers in the mathematical sciences.* Faculty improvement is essential; and specific kinds of support of early graduate work can avoid losses, both of people and of opportunities for sound training. (See Recommendations 14 through 17 and the report[1] of our Panel on Undergraduate Education.)

Maintenance of momentum in research, research apprenticeship, and graduate education. This will require continuing growth in federal support of these activities. Even if this is provided, the mathematical community will not grow fast enough to meet national needs. Accordingly, recent slackening in federal support† are a cause of deep concern to the mathematical community and should, we feel, be a matter of general concern. (See Recommendations 1 and 11 through 13.)

Support for the explosive growth of computer science, especially

* This is documented and discussed in Chapter 7 under Quality and Distribution of Mathematical-Science Faculty (see page 127) as well as in the report[1] of our Panel on Undergraduate Education.
† See reference 2, Volume XVI, Appendix C.

as a field of research in its own right. (See Recommendations 2, 3, and 19.)

Support of research and education in the applied mathematical sciences as such, and not merely in connection with either mathematics or the particular sciences that use mathematics. Such support will not be expensive, but a failure to seize today's opportunity would be costly. (See Recommendations 4, 18, 21, and 22.)

Agencies and mechanisms for federal support of research and research apprenticeship in the mathematical sciences. (See Recommendations 5 through 10.)

A continuing program of information-gathering about research and education in the mathematical sciences. (See Recommendation 20.)

RESEARCH

The encouragement and support that the research effort in the mathematical sciences has received during the last 20 years in the United States have made this effort eminently successful by any test. The record shows numerous and great intellectual achievements as well as substantial material and social benefits resulting directly from the endeavors thus set in motion. The United States now holds a position of leadership in all mathematical sciences. To prepare for future needs, the momentum of research should be preserved.

Growth and Level

Federal support of research and research apprenticeship in the mathematical sciences has developed and nurtured a process of growth limited more by natural abilities and by individual preferences among fields than by available funds. Even if this momentum continues, the mathematical community will not grow fast enough to meet national needs.

1. We recommend that, as a national policy, federal support for basic research and research apprenticeship in the mathematical sciences and in each of their major subdivisions—including the areas of core mathematics—continue to grow in proportion to the number of appropriately qualified investigators and graduate students.

DISCUSSION   An analysis of the present level of support for research in the mathematical sciences is presented in Chapter 10. An extraordinary development of mathematical competence and prestige has accompanied modest expenditures: a relatively small (approximately $15 million in 1966) annual investment by the National Science Foundation in academic mathematical research, a larger total investment in basic mathematical research at universities (approximately $35 million in 1966) by all federal agencies,* the much larger government investment in both basic and applied research in the mathematical sciences (approximately $125 million in 1966). Vastly larger investments (e.g., $2 billion estimated for the purchase and utilization of computers by the government in 1967) are importantly affected in their effective use by research in the mathematical sciences.

The ratio of the national investment in basic research to the investment in fields of application is so small, and the benefits from basic research so large, that the goal of programs for the support of basic mathematical research, in core mathematics and in the applied mathematical sciences, should be limited only by the availability of high-quality investigators.

We estimate that at present about one out of every six PhD's in the mathematical sciences is consistently active in research. Over the past five years the number of PhD's has been growing at an average rate of 18 percent per year; a rate of at least 10 percent is projected for the next five years (see Chapter 8). We believe that throughout the next decade the increase of qualified investigators in the mathematical sciences will lag substantially behind society's need.

We consider that the level and rate of growth of support was adequate a few years ago—at least within the core areas. (In the other mathematical sciences there has been a shortage of funds for basic research not tied to specific applications. In computer science the support for unrestricted basic research in the software area has been quite inadequate.) At present the failure of current and projected budgets to provide expansion adequate to take account of larger numbers of qualified mathematicians, advancing costs of research, and advancing overhead rates is a matter of serious concern. The above recommendation can be thought of as urging the

---

* For 1966 the $35 million spent in basic academic mathematical research was 2.4 percent of the total federal research expenditures in that year.

maintenance of at least a *natural rate of growth* throughout the mathematical sciences.

The Special Situation of Computer Science

National needs and developments in contemporary technology require the stimulation of higher than natural rates of progress in some areas of the mathematical sciences. Of particular urgency at this time are the requirements of computer science.

2. *We recommend that at the national level special priority be given to support of the expansion of research and graduate study in computer science. Appropriate actions would include: special support for developing and updating courses, support for research during the academic year when needed, grants to departments to cover costs of computer usage in research, special attention to needs for space, and expansion of numbers of research assistantships and traineeships to stretch the capacity of all departments of high quality.*

DISCUSSION   The proliferation of high-speed electronic data-processing equipment, combined with the rapidly expanding art of its use, constitutes one of the newest and most dynamic forces affecting the mathematical sciences. There is a critical shortage of research leaders in computer science, and urgent steps are required to overcome it as fast as possible. Electronic computers have evolved so rapidly that in many areas they have become an integral part of operations before there has been time for the research needed to determine the best, or even fairly good, ways of using them. The vast expenditures for computing in the operations of the federal government alone mean that even modest improvements achievable from research at relatively low cost will almost surely pay off in large cost reductions and improvements in service within a very few years. Despite the large sums available to finance computing service on campus, the money available for research in computer science has been, with the exception of a few spectacular projects, seriously inadequate.

* * *

The role of computers in higher education across the board has recently been studied in the Pierce report[3] of the President's Science Advisory Committee. The detailed impact of projections made by this and similar studies on the requirements for research and education in computer science itself is, however, most inadequately understood. This matter obviously demands urgent attention.

3. We recommend a thorough study of the implications for research and advanced education in computer science of an adequate implementation of the recommendations of the Pierce report.[3]

Basic Research in Applied Mathematics

Research of sufficiently high quality is wisely supported as research for its own sake. In at least two areas of applied mathematics—physical mathematics (sometimes called classical applied mathematics) and the mathematics underlying operations research and modern economics—there are growing communities of mathematical scientists whose efforts meet this criterion. Their basic research should thus be supported partly for its own sake and as a field in its own right, rather than solely because of its immediately perceived contributions to particular fields of application.

4. We recommend that federal support for research and research apprenticeship in high-quality basic applied mathematics be given on the basis of intellectual worth (recognizing, of course, the overall importance of progress in applied mathematics to many sciences).

DISCUSSION   There is a significant distinction between such applied mathematical sciences as physical mathematics and the mathematics underlying operations research and such partly mathematical sciences as statistics and computer science. Mathematics is applied in all these disciplines, as it is in so many others. The partly mathematical sciences gain their identity—and their only partly mathematical nature—from the existence of problems, not initially mathematical, that run broadly through most fields of science and technology. The applied mathematical sciences, like physical mathematics and operations research, have had the effect of uniting mathematics with specific areas of application—an effect that will not disappear. However, they have not developed a sufficiently strong identity of their own. Much can be gained from the development of such identities, the foundations for which already exist in intellectually worthwhile research of high quality. Recent work, characterized by the evolution of ever more appropriate mathematical models, together with the evolution of mathematical techniques,* display clearly the comprehensive nature of the discipline of applied mathematics. Support of such work for its own sake is now clearly justified and need not interfere with other work in these areas supported because of its more immediate usefulness.

Sources of Support

The major federal support of research and higher education in the mathematical sciences comes from a variety of agencies, the most important being the National Science Foundation and certain of the mission-oriented agencies, as indicated in more detail in Chapters 10 and 11. We believe that activities in the mathematical sciences will continue to be relevant to the tasks of all these agencies, and that all of them should continue to share in the future support of these sciences.

5. *We recommend a level of growth that will enable the National Science Foundation to continue effectively in its central role in support of basic research and higher education in the mathematical sciences.*

DISCUSSION The National Science Foundation is the agency of the federal government whose direct mission is the promotion and support of basic research and education in the sciences. In carrying out this mission it has evolved a versatile and highly effective array of programs. A vital ingredient in the success of these programs has been the system of peer-evaluation for ensuring high quality in the research and educational activities supported.

The National Science Foundation has been a very important source of support for the mathematical sciences, furnishing in recent years close to one third of the total federal support of mathematical activities in basic research and approximately half of the federal support specifically allotted to mathematical activities in higher education. As the sum total of our discussion in various parts

---

* In studies, for example, of the dynamics of the ocean, the structure of galaxies, the physics of low-density gases, and the optimal use of water-supply systems.

of the present report indicates, we feel that the whole range of National Science Foundation programs in the mathematical sciences has been valuable and well conceived. We urge a natural rate of growth in most of these programs and a more rapid growth in several. We also suggest a few new programs.

* * *

Several mission-oriented agencies of the government rely on advanced mathematical techniques in accomplishing their tasks. For such agencies it is important to maintain close contact with contemporary activity and competence in the mathematical sciences.

6. We recommend that mission-oriented agencies that expect to derive significant benefits from the use of mathematical sciences continue and expand their partnership with the community of mathematicians by:

(a) participating in the sponsorship, not only of research that promises predictable returns in applications, but also of basic investigations that enlarge the intellectual foundations of the field, and

(b) evolving organized plans for bringing their unsolved scientific problems to the attention of the mathematical-sciences community and for providing the opportunity to qualified research mathematicians to further, at times and in the depth of their choosing, the mathematization of major realms of scientific and technical effort of national concern.

DISCUSSION The past record of sponsorship of mathematics research by the mission-oriented agencies shows its effectiveness. The possibility of rapid adaptation and follow-through in connection with newly developed techniques of mathematical analysis has greatly assisted the mission-oriented agencies; and familiarity with some of the difficult scientific and technological obstacles that must be overcome has been instrumental in stimulating fruitful fundamental research endeavors.

Time may be lost and effort wasted in the achievement of technology-dependent objectives, and delays may occur in the progress of mathematical techniques for the advancement of other sciences, if we fail to develop and to maintain continuing channels of communication between the mathematicians and the heavy users of mathematical sciences. Thus we believe that it is vital to continue, and to strengthen where it is already established this pattern of cooperation between mission-oriented agencies and the mathematical community, and to extend it further as our national commitments venture into areas in which the role played by science and technology becomes ever more intricate. Areas of possible expansion include housing and urban development, transportation, management of this country's natural resources, and the guidance of its educational efforts.

* * *

Of the federally sponsored research in the mathematical sciences, reported as basic by the supporting agencies, 60 percent is conducted in academic institutions. Of this fraction, a little less than one half is supported by the National Science Foundation. Other agencies, mainly the Department of Defense, the Atomic Energy Commission, and the National Aeronautics and Space Administration, account for the remainder of the university research and for the bulk of the basic work conducted under government sponsorship at nonacademic establishments, amounting to just under three fourths of the total federal commitment to basic research in the mathematical sciences.

7. We recommend that the Department of Defense, the Atomic Energy Commission, the National Aeronautics and Space Administration, and the National Institutes of Health continue programs for the sponsorship of basic research in the mathematical sciences, and especially in physical and engineering mathematics, statistics, computer science, and operations research and management science. This support should increase at rates that will enable these agencies to share responsibly in maintaining at least the natural growth rate and that provide for higher rates of expansion in areas with long-term relevance to the agency's mission.

DISCUSSION   At issue here for the most part is basic research, conducted at universities, government laboratories, and industrial establishments in the areas of applied mathematics and statistics, computer science, and operations research and management science. The Department of Defense has the longest history of cooperation with the community of mathematics, and there can be no question that over the years defense technology has benefited in many and vital ways therefrom (e.g., in computer and communications technology, quality control and life testing, and programming of massive supply operations).

The agencies in question bear an important share in the stewardship of one of this country's vital resources—its research potential in the mathematical sciences. Moreover, the multiple character of the support has itself contributed greatly to the vigorous state of American mathematics.

Forms of Support*

Since World War II, the overwhelming bulk of federal support of research in mathematical sciences has been support of individual or group projects. Two decades of experience have demonstrated the effectiveness of the project system.

8. We recommend that federal agencies sponsoring basic academic research in the mathematical sciences continue to use the project system as the primary mechanism for support.

DISCUSSION   The project system has proved compatible with almost every pattern of departmental university organization; it has also proved flexible in adjustment to the tasks required and effective in linking the problems of sponsoring agencies with relevant contemporary mathematical research. A more detailed discussion and evaluation of the project system is given in Chapter 10.

*   *   *

We believe, however, that project grants and contracts are not always best suited for fulfilling several necessary tasks: assisting departments of quality and promise to become truly outstanding, developing new centers of leadership in the applied mathematical sciences, and providing centers of research and graduate education in geographical regions so far deprived of them.

* This committee is aware that authoritative voices have proposed very radical revisions of the whole federal system for supporting academic research and university education, abandoning the present forms of support in favor of direct federal subsidy to universities. We feel that a discussion of this problem lies outside our competence. The fact that we do not mention these possibilities in our report, however, should not be taken as evidence that we oppose them. It is self-evident that in any thorough discussion of such radical changes the special problems of the mathematical sciences would have to be taken into account.

9. We recommend increased exploitation of departmental grants to supplement the traditional project grants and the recently established university science development awards.

DISCUSSION The departmental grant provides a mechanism for support of the mathematical sciences with desirable flexibility in meeting the diverse needs and capacities for academic mathematical research. The university science development grants have proved useful for the support of research and graduate educational activities that correlate well with those of other departments. In the mathematical sciences these have usually tended to be better suited to the needs of computing, statistics, and traditional applied mathematics than to those of core mathematics. The departmental grants should extend such opportunities to core mathematics, as well as permitting other areas of the mathematical sciences to develop their identities and programs.*

Peer Evaluation

Federal support of basic academic research has relied on judgment by qualified investigators in the evaluation of proposals for research grants as well as in processing applications for fellowships. This practice is doubtless one reason why such support has worked as well as it has.

10. We recommend that the principle of peer judgment continue to be used with respect to all forms of support for basic academic research and research education. An essential part of peer judgment should be representation of specialized areas, especially applied mathematical sciences, on evaluation groups that are likely to deal with applications from these areas.

DISCUSSION The purpose of such representation is to ensure that proposals from an area of specialization receive a fair evaluation by people familiar with the aims and standards of the field. (The range of judgment required in peer evaluation is indicated by the

---

* We are aware of the twin dangers of "gimmickitis" and "hit and run" financing so eloquently described by George Pake ["Basic Research and Financial Crisis in the Universities," *Science*, *157*, 517–520 (Aug. 4, 1967)]. We hope that programs of departmental grants (and indeed all grants) will be so administered as to minimize these dangers.

occurrence of both physical mathematics and mathematical logic among the mathematical sciences.) Efforts in this direction are being made at present, yet it is important to adhere to the principle that justice not only be done but also be seen to be done.

EDUCATION

Research Apprenticeship

We believe, as already stated, that for the foreseeable future this country will need every qualified investigator it can educate in the mathematical sciences. An even more critical need is for college teachers. Our estimate is that 8,000 new teachers of mathematical sciences will be needed in the four-year colleges and universities by 1971 (see Chapter 7). These two needs cannot be discussed separately, since at this level of education it is impossible to foresee which students will eventually do research, which will teach, and which will do both. Therefore, we consider it to be in the national interest that every student capable of and interested in earning a PhD degree in the mathematical sciences should have available to him the support required for achieving this goal.

11. We recommend that federal support, combining research assistantships, fellowships, and traineeships, provide support for at least one third of the expanding full-time graduate student population in the mathematical sciences, and that the number of research assistantships under grants and contracts be not less than the number of senior investigators supported.

DISCUSSION In the academic year 1965–1966, about 28 percent of the roughly 9,400 full-time graduate students in the mathematical sciences received some form of federal support: 13 percent through fellowships, 7 percent through traineeships, and 8 percent through research assistantships (see Table 16, page 181). The number of research assistantships probably is now about three quarters of the number of senior investigators working on grants and contracts. Computer science, applied mathematics, and statistics support a higher than average proportion of their students through research assistantships. Core mathematics, on the other hand, employs a higher proportion of graduate students as teaching assistants; 38

percent of all graduate students in the mathematical sciences are employed as teaching assistants.

We believe that there are cogent reasons for increasing the number of research assistantships in all the mathematical sciences. Such assistantships serve several useful purposes. They bring graduate students into direct and immediate contact with active mathematicians and introduce them, at an early stage, to the spirit and techniques of independent work. At the same time, most mature investigators find such contact with young colleagues stimulating and useful for their own work. It should be noted that in mathematics a research assistant is almost always an apprentice and a junior participant in a joint intellectual undertaking, rather than a mere agent performing tasks useful for the research of his principal. It hardly ever happens that the research assistant is prevented or discouraged from following his own scientific interests. (As a matter of fact, PhD candidates supported by fellowships and traineeships often act, in effect, as research assistants.) Curtailing the number of research assistantships, unfortunately, has become almost a standard response to budgetary limitations.

This committee believes that practically all PhD candidates should do some teaching sometime during their graduate work. We deplore the fact, however, that at present some graduate students teach throughout their graduate careers, while others do no teaching at all. We suggest that universities, in cooperation with relevant government agencies, strive toward a system in which every graduate student acquires teaching experience during some years in graduate school (whether by teaching a section, leading recitation groups, or doing informal instruction) and in which no student's progress toward receiving the PhD degree is impeded by an excessive teaching load.

*   *   *

Ordinarily, a student in the mathematical sciences receives his doctorate before he has completed an adequate professional apprenticeship. Furthermore, students who plan careers that involve the applications of mathematics in broad areas have not ordinarily acquired an adequate acquaintance with the attitudes, objectives, and foundations of some of the relevant sciences. Clearly, then, we must recognize the need for postdoctoral educational avenues toward professional maturity. These include appointments both for pure research and for research and teaching combined.

12. We recommend the continuation and, wherever possible, expansion of existing opportunities for postdoctoral study.

In addition, we recommend a new program of postdoctoral research instructorships (50 each year for a two-year term) whose holders will teach at smaller colleges and conduct research at nearby centers.

DISCUSSION It is the view of this committee that the number of postdoctoral research appointments should be substantially expanded. For many capable young PhD's a postdoctoral position that involves both teaching and research can be very beneficial. Such young PhD's should also be encouraged to seek positions in a broader variety of colleges and universities. The second part of the above recommendation, coming from our Panel on Undergraduate Education, is one of several plans suggested to the Committee for achieving this end. We feel that while other proposals merit study, this particular one calls for immediate implementation.

* * *

At present we are making a most ineffective use of the intellectual potential of women. (See the discussion in the report[1] of our Panel on Undergraduate Education.)

13. We recommend a special program for part-time graduate fellowships, available to women who have completed their master's degrees or met equivalent requirements.

DISCUSSION A much smaller proportion of women than of men go beyond the master's degree to the PhD degree in the mathematical sciences. Because of social pressures and family obligations, it is generally much harder for a woman than for a man to qualify for support, which usually demands full-time graduate study. A significant increase in the number of mathematical scientists with advanced training could be made if the potential of mathematically talented women were used more fully. The suggested program is a modest step in this direction.

The Committee also suggests that universities and state authorities abolish out-dated nepotism rules, which often prevent qualified women mathematicians from seeking academic employment, and that part-time academic employment for women be made more widely available.

Early Graduate Education

Today, federal support of graduate students goes primarily to candidates for the PhD degree; we feel that this support should be extended to other graduate students.

14. We recommend an experimental program for federal support of graduate students in qualified institutions that do not offer a PhD degree in mathematical sciences.

DISCUSSION By 1970, two out of three first-year graduate students will be in institutions not granting the PhD degree, if present trends continue. Many of these will receive their doctorates elsewhere. It is important that institutions should be encouraged to strengthen their programs in early graduate education, without prematurely embarking on PhD programs themselves.

Also, colleges, and especially the growing junior colleges, make extensive use of holders of the master's degree as faculty members. Many with master's level training are employed in industry as well.

* * *

We find that a substantial preventable loss of mathematical talent occurs between college and graduate school because of inadequate undergraduate preparation.

15. We recommend special fellowships, or forgivable loans, for talented college graduates with weak or inadequate preparation in the mathematical sciences, to enable them to begin graduate work.

We recommend that graduate departments in the mathematical sciences be encouraged to make special efforts to admit talented college graduates with weak or inadequate preparation in the mathematical sciences and to provide suitable educational programs for such students after their admission.

DISCUSSION The faculties of many colleges are too small or too poorly prepared to offer their students adequate preparation for modern graduate work in the mathematical sciences. (These include most of the approximately 600 colleges that have at most one mathematics teacher with a PhD degree.) A graduate of such a college is likely to find difficulty in obtaining admission to a graduate school in the mathematical sciences. And, even if admitted, he

is apt to have serious difficulty with the normal program planned
for first-year graduate students. Such a student needs a chance to
move into a college or university through special programs planned
to bring his background up to the normal standard for entering
graduate students. Such programs for talented students with weak
preparation would be especially suitable for colleges or universities
having strong master's programs in mathematical sciences, but no
PhD programs.

Faculty Improvement

In recent years, universities and colleges have been beset by the
challenges of enrollment increases and curriculum revisions, both
undergraduate and graduate. For the mathematical sciences these
challenges have been underlined by an extraordinary growth in the
number of student majors, by rapid and extensive developments in
subject matter, and by increases in numbers of majors in other
fields who elect courses in the mathematical sciences, sometimes for
cultural reasons but more often for their usefulness in those other
fields (see discussions of The Increase in Mathematical Majors,
page 122; Total Enrollments in the Mathematical Sciences, page 124;
and The College Teacher, page 147).

If these challenges are even partially to be met, it is imperative
that, along with educating new college teachers of the mathematical
sciences, special efforts be made to upgrade and update present
college faculties, with special emphasis on current developments in
the mathematical sciences and their penetration into new areas of
application.

*16. We recommend that the National Science Foundation Science
Faculty Fellowship Program be gradually expanded to provide by
1971 at least 150 awards in the mathematical sciences—roughly
double the number in recent years.*

DISCUSSION Our Panel on Undergraduate Education has estimated
that a program of this expanded size would offer opportunity for
awards to approximately one quarter of the doctorate-holding faculty and one half of the nondoctorate-holding factulty at least once
in their teaching careers. Clearly this is a conservative goal; it would
be desirable to exceed it if conditions permit.

*   *   *

The problem of upgrading and updating college faculty in the mathematical sciences is too massive to be fully met by academic-year programs like the National Science Foundation Science Faculty Fellowship Program. This is especially true of further faculty training in certain areas of rapidly increasing demand, such as linear algebra, probability and statistics, computer science, and applications of mathematics in the physical, biological, and social sciences.

17. We recommend the expansion of programs of summer institutes for college teachers, and especially programs in areas of increasing demand where additional faculty competence is most needed.

DISCUSSION This too is one of the recommendations of our Panel on Undergraduate Education. As the Panel points out, the over-all shortage of college teachers of mathematics is aggravated by their insufficient familiarity with special subject-matter areas, most notably in the fields named under Recommendation 16 above. See the discussion of The College Teacher on page 147, references 4 and 5, and the report[1] of our Panel on Undergraduate Education.

Undergraduate Education in Applied Mathematical Sciences

Applied mathematics as a science and an art with its own objectives, attitudes, and skills has lagged badly. Only a relatively few pioneers who have seen the need and the opportunity have striven to acquire and to teach a comprehensive view of the manner in which mathematics is applied to many fields of science.

18. We recommend that the federal government give active support to the development generally, but especially at the undergraduate level, of experimental educational programs that stress the common features of the applications of mathematics.

DISCUSSION Much could be gained if it were possible to develop not only the individual identities associated with different fields of application but also a single identity that would emphasize *in breadth* the application of mathematics in the physical sciences, in the biological and behavioral sciences, in engineering and medicine, and in the partly mathematical sciences. We do not yet know how effectively this can be done. Experimentation is needed. Such experimentation deserves, and will require, support from both the universities and the federal government.

Efforts of this comprehensive character are especially important at the undergraduate level where they can provide (a) the educational foundations for graduate work and subsequently a career in the applied mathematical sciences, (b) the augmentation, both in substance and perspective, of curricula in more specialized disciplines, and (c) an undergraduate program offering an additional route to graduate study in any of the particular, more specialized mathematical sciences or in the partly mathematical sciences.

* * *

At present, in many universities and colleges, students receive an excellent preparation for graduate work in core mathematics, but a traditional mathematics major program may not be the only way or the best way of attracting and motivating an undergraduate for further work in the partly mathematical sciences.

19. We recommend that special attention and, where needed, federal support be given to undergraduate programs in the partly mathematical sciences. This would include (a) more active participation of existing statistics departments in undergraduate education, (b) development of undergraduate programs in operations research and management science, and (c) development of more undergraduate programs in computer science.

DISCUSSION In statistics, there is a shortage of graduate students; one reason for this is the lack of undergraduate programs in the field. Since there is a fair number of separate statistics departments, the remedy and the decision lie in their hands.

In computer science the rate of founding of new graduate departments is already straining the supply of qualified faculty. On the undergraduate level, however, much could be done by using existing faculty in other departments or by drawing part-time faculty from local industry. Federal support may be needed (a) for the preparation and updating of specialized courses and (b) for student computer use.

The augmentations of undergraduate education called for in Recommendations 18 and 19 must be consistent with the broad general goals of education at this level. In consideration of this, many institutions will find that increased flexibility and increased breadth in existing programs, rather than the introduction of new majors, will meet the need.

SURVEYS AND STUDIES

There are important issues that cannot be resolved at this time because they require further investigations. Although these issues are widely disparate, we present them together here (see also Recommendation 3).

Continuing Survey Activities in the Mathematical Sciences

On many occasions the Committee on Support of Research in the Mathematical Sciences (COSRIMS) and the Survey Committee of the Conference Board of the Mathematical Sciences (CBMS) have found themselves balked by unavailability of reliable data of the most basic kind. The multiplicity of agency administrative and fiscal arrangements and the widely differing policies and practices used in classifying research and in accounting for manpower strengths and requirements in the mathematical sciences have made it hard to develop reliable data.

20. We recommend that surveys of activities in research and education in the mathematical sciences, such as those that have supported the work of this committee, be put on a continuing basis, perhaps under the leadership of the Conference Board of the Mathematical Sciences.

Mathematical Sciences in Government Research and Development Establishments

Examples from major industries, notably the Bell Telephone Laboratories and the Boeing Aircraft Company, have shown how the imaginative employment of mathematical techniques contributes to the development of new capabilities based on sophisticated technology. In the early 1950's, the Mathematics Division of the National Bureau of Standards very effectively served this role for the U.S. Government. As its needs for mathematical techniques have grown, however, the government has come increasingly to rely on outside contractors rather than on the expansion of mathematical resources within its own research and development establishments.

21. *We recommend that a broadly qualified* ad hoc *group be convened to study the desirability and feasibility of creating research units within one or a few of the government's key research and development establishments whose mission would be the development and imaginative application of mathematical-science results and techniques in contexts pertinent to federal efforts.*

New National Goals

Growing up alongside the national programs that call for physics and heavy engineering, there are now programs that, with increasing frequency, receive at least equal priority and that are designed to ameliorate the lives of individuals or to develop beneficial social organizations, and hence involve the problems of environment and people. The use of mathematical techniques in these contexts can be very substantial and must be expected to depend largely on the applications that are made of electronic data-processing facilities as well as the constructions of systems analysis, operations research, and the management sciences.

22. *We recommend that recently established agencies of the federal government, whose missions strongly depend on science and technology, cooperate with the National Science Foundation in a thorough review of those activities in the mathematical sciences that deserve attention in the context of their missions.*

IMPLICATIONS FOR PROGRAM AND RESOURCES PLANNING

Most of the recommendations of the previous sections make budgeting and policy demands on the conduct of the federally sponsored research and advanced education programs in the mathematical sciences. Relevant information and data have been developed throughout the report. For the convenience of program planners and managers, the key elements are summarized here in direct juxtaposition with our key recommendations.

The baseline for our projections is constituted by the allocations of fiscal year 1966, the last complete year for which data became available while the present survey was in progress. For that year, the agencies of the federal government reported research and development obligations totaling $125 million for research in the mathematical sciences. Of this amount a conservative estimate identifies at least $45 million as having been spent on basic research. The remainder of $80 million has served to fund applied research directly supporting the missions of the sponsoring agencies, as well as a few major projects—principally under the aegis of the Advanced Research Projects Agency of the Department of Defense—in which it proved impossible to separate basic from applied components. No long-term rates of growth have been projected for this remainder item; its future level will be established by the needs and opportunities as they are identified by the individual agencies.

Returning to the allocation of $45 million to basic research in 1966, we have estimated that about $35 million of this went for the support of academic research, leaving a remainder of roughly $10 million for the conduct of basic mathematical-sciences research under programs administered at the local level by the major federally sponsored research and development centers. Again, no attempt has been made to project the growth of this fraction over the next few years. Within the $35 million for academic research, we have identified slightly over $20 million as allocated to project support, the remainder accounting for other than project-type support, such as portions of interdisciplinary efforts, departmental and institutional grants, and conference activities.

In addition to the $125 million in research and development obligations in base year 1966, approximately $10 million of other federal funds were allocated in that year to the support of graduate study in the mathematical sciences and approximately $5 million to programs of further faculty training and various activities in undergraduate educational improvement in these fields. Our recommendations dealing with levels and forms of support are addressed principally to the budget for academic research ($35 million in 1966) and for these closely related items in higher education ($15 million in 1966).

The Staffing of the Colleges; Research and Research Education

The current level and rate of growth of the demand for professional competence in the mathematical sciences to conduct research and research education has been estimated in connection with:

(a) Projected requirements for the teaching of mathematical sciences at the college level;

(b) The funding of applied research in the mathematical sciences by the mission-oriented agencies of the federal government;

(c) Manpower demands in certain of the applied mathematical sciences, especially computer science and those intervening in the field of operations research.

Conservative estimates anticipate a need of some 8,000 additional full-time college faculty members by the academic year 1970–1971 over the 10,750 in service in 1965–1966. According to these estimates only about 41 percent of these new faculty members will have doctorates, even on the optimistic assumption that in the intervening five years no less than 70 percent of the new PhD's will be teaching mathematical sciences at universities and four-year colleges. This would represent a lowering of quality in the sense that currently 46 percent of those teaching the mathematical sciences in universities and four-year colleges have PhD degrees in the mathematical sciences. (Another 6 percent have PhD degrees in other fields, primarily education.)

Government support of applied research in the mathematical sciences has grown at an average rate of 51 percent per year during the period 1960 to 1966, largely because of rapidly increasing commitments in computer research and development and in operations research. Having now reached a level of about $80 million per year, this support shows a slackening growth rate, which is, however, still running well ahead of the annual growth rate for support of basic research. Correspondingly, growing manpower demands in the applied mathematical sciences indicate that current shortages will become even more severe in the next few years.

Thus, shortages of mathematical manpower, for both teaching and research, are increasing. These are occurring in spite of a relatively high rate of growth in PhD production during recent years—averaging 18 percent per year over the period 1960–1965—and in spite of the fact that not many capable graduate students appear to have been lost because of lack of support during that period.

As a consequence, we have had to conclude that even optimal planning and management of sponsored programs in research and professional education will not build up the mathematical-sciences community fast enough to meet national needs. It is therefore important that economic deterrents not retard the replenishment of the group on which the responsibility for innovation, research training, and college education devolves. Hence, our recommendations (Recommendations 1, 8, 9, and 11) call for an expansion in the support of basic academic research and research apprenticeship in the mathematical sciences at least at a rate that will not interpose economic barriers to the achievement of competence in research and research education.

In the absence of much of the necessary information, only relatively crude planning factors can be established. Taking Recommendations 1 and 11 together because they involve common elements, we estimate that:

(a) In the $20 million worth of project research, a total of approximately 920 tenure research investigators (TRI) participated, so that the average expenditure of such funds (investigators' salaries, visitors, research associates and assistants, secretarial support, publication, overhead) amounted to around $22,000 per TRI.

(b) One out of six PhD's in the mathematical sciences ends up doing research found worthy of support. Allowing for the elapse of approximately five years between receipt of the doctorate and the acquisition of tenure, the figures on earned doctorates provide an estimate of approximately 1,400 for the group of TRI's by 1971.

(c) The planning factor of $22,000 per TRI will grow, because of (i) the increasing cost of research, which is certainly no less than 4 percent per year, (ii) the cost of growing requirements for machine computing, which cannot be reliably estimated at present but, in particular instances, reach magnitudes that dwarf all other costs, and, finally, (iii) the increase in the number of research assistants per TRI called for by Recommendation 11. We arrive, conservatively, at a minimum of $29,000 per TRI by 1971.*

(d) Comparable growth should be provided in the nonproject forms of academic research support, under the assumption that no

---

* In computer science itself the corresponding average annual cost is estimated in the section on Computer Science (page 205) to be approximately $60,000 per TRI.

radical change is made in the balance with project support (Recommendation 9).

(e) Graduate-student enrollment will grow from its 1966 level of 9,400 to approximately 18,400 by 1971. With 1,300 covered by research assistantships [see (b) above], a total of 4,800 will have to be accommodated by fellowship and traineeship programs if one third of them are to be given research apprenticeship support, in accordance with Recommendation 11. The corresponding figure for 1966 is 1,834, and the at least 4 percent per year increase in cost of research also affects the rate per research apprentice in these programs.

Total costs can now be projected for 1971 and converted into an annual percent rate of growth for the period 1966–1971. Specifically, there would be $66 million for academic research, of which at least $38 million would be in the form of project research, and another $30 million in fellowship and traineeship support. The equivalent annual growth rates turn out to be 14 percent for research, 24 percent for research apprenticeship, and 16 percent overall.* Of special significance and thus to be emphasized is the relatively greater increase in support for research apprenticeship than for research, in order to prepare for meeting national needs in the mid-1970's.

---

* There is another, simpler, kind of calculation that also leads to this over-all annual growth rate for the period 1966–1971. The Westheimer report[6] on chemistry (page 166) tied PhD production to total federal obligations for basic research in the field, leading to a figure for "Federal support cost per PhD produced." For 1962, the year reported on in the Westheimer report, the mathematical sciences had the lowest such cost, namely approximately

$$\frac{\$22.6 \text{ million}}{410 \text{ PhD's}} = \$55,000/\text{PhD.}$$

For 1966, we find that it was approximately

$$\frac{\$50 \text{ million}}{770 \text{ PhD's}} = \$65,000/\text{PhD,}$$

indicating that from 1962 to 1966 the cost per PhD had increased by approximately 4 percent per year. Supposing it to continue to increase at this rate, this cost will be approximately $80,000/PhD by 1971. With about 1,300 PhD's projected to be produced in 1971, this gives, for federal support of basic research in 1971,

$$\$80,000/\text{PhD} \times 1,300 \text{ PhD's} = \$104 \text{ million.}$$

This is slightly more than double the 1966 figure and may be computed to call for growth at an average annual rate of just about 16 percent.

The final sense of our recommendations, however, does not lie in these particular figures but in identifying the factors that must serve to determine them. As our knowledge regarding the latter improves, both budget projections and growth rates can be adjusted accordingly. Hence, our recommendations (especially Recommendations 3 and 20) call for continuing efforts of investigation and analysis to develop suitable planning factors and information about research and education in the mathematical sciences so that evolving needs and trends can be appraised more reliably.

As the demand for mathematical-science instructors with PhD education will continue to outrun supply in the shorter time frame in any case, their number must be increased by using opportunities that have so far been neglected for one reason or another. Particular programs toward such an end are the subject of Recommendations 13 and 14. For the 50 postdoctoral teaching fellowships of Recommendation 12, the cost of supplementary stipends (about $8–9 thousand each) and administration should not exceed $600 thousand per year. The special part-time graduate fellowships for women under Recommendation 13 would constitute about 10 percent of all available full-time graduate fellowships in the mathematical sciences, i.e., about 100 initially and perhaps 200 five years hence. Cost, including administration, would range correspondingly from $300 thousand to $600 thousand.

In addition to the need for a basic policy that maintains the present momentum of research and research apprenticeship in the mathematical sciences across the board, our recommendations recognize certain critical areas in which more than ordinary efforts are needed if the mathematical-sciences community is to render the required services in today's social fabric. These are Recommendations 2, 3, and 4 relating to the support of research and research education in computer science and in the applied mathematical sciences as such.

Planning factors to gauge the development of research and research education in computer science are provided by the size, the cost, and the growth rate of this country's computer establishment. It is clear that it will be some time before the schools and universities will have caught up even approximately with the requirements that this is generating. Not the least among these is the growing use of computers in the educational process itself, the full-scale expansion of which has been recommended by the President's Science Advisory Committee in the Pierce report.[3] At the same time, the availability of support for computer science as a field of research in its own right has been minuscule in comparison to its economic and intellectual importance. Under the conditions, there is no choice except to stretch the capacity of high-quality departments as far as this is possible with resources in faculty, space, and computer facilities, potentially available to them, in order to engage in original research and, especially, to create opportunities for research apprenticeship.

The appropriate level of support for such programs is notoriously difficult to project, one of the more recent proposals suggesting that it be made a flat percentage (e.g., 5 percent) of the $415 million estimated by the Pierce report as being required by 1971 to cover the educational use of computers in universities. There are at present a dozen or more departments of computer science that would qualify for support under Recommendation 2; five years from now, their number may well have tripled. This suggests a program, starting at $6 million and stabilizing at $15–20 million no later than five years hence. If, however, the doubling time of the number of eligible departments should be two years, rather than the three years estimated above, these projections would represent gross underestimates for the latter years.

In contrast, the support of a few research and research training programs of exceptional quality in the applied mathematical sciences for their own sake will be of low cost. There are today probably no more than half a dozen universities that would qualify for such a program. Program cost would therefore amount to an initial $500,000, growing to $1.5–2 million per year in the course of the next three or four years and stabilizing at that point.

Undergraduate and Early Graduate Education

Of the recommendations in these critical areas, three relate to faculty improvement in undergraduate colleges. Two of these (Recommendations 16 and 17) call for appropriately directed expansion of existing programs. Doubling in the course of five years the number of available National Science Foundation Science Faculty Fellowships in the mathematical sciences alone would increase the program by only about $1.5 million a year. Planning in this connection, however, will have to take into consideration the Science Faculty Fellowship program as a whole in the establishment of proper balances. With respect to summer institutes, as proposed in Recommendation

17, the underlying current estimates are that, of the roughly 10,000 college teachers in the mathematical sciences, approximately 10 percent should have the opportunity each year of participating in summer institutes. Effective training groups run about 30 students each, which would lead to some 35 institutes per summer, tripling the currently supported number. Costs per institute will range from $70,000 to $100,000, so that initial program totals would lie at around $3 million, rising in future years.

Recommendations 14 and 15 propose certain forms of student assistance. Neither of these programs is likely to be very expensive. The support of graduate students in colleges and universities, offering no PhD degree but a high-quality master's degree in the mathematical sciences, is meant to be experimental and therefore limited to perhaps 15 to 20 typical such schools. The program of special fellowships or forgivable loans to promising students, emerging from colleges with inadequate departments in the mathematical sciences, would be gauged to make 200 awards per year at a total program cost of $1 million.

The development, finally, of undergraduate programs in the applied mathematical sciences is largely an internal decision of university administrations, which might be expedited only peripherally by the possibility of federal support. If the primary resources exist to offer such programs—be they in comprehensive applied mathematics, statistics, computer science, or operations research—the difference of providing the necessary management, housekeeping, office and classroom space, and other facilities is more a matter of support of university infrastructure as a whole than of particular fields. The moral pressure of concerned interest, backed up as necessary by an occasional subsidy of the right sort, is all that is needed to implement Recommendation 19.

Applied Research

Applied research in the mathematical sciences, supported by mission-oriented agencies in the context of and for immediate utilization in specific applications of significance to the sponsoring agency, is of very recent origin. As late as 1960, it amounted to no more than $6.6 million out of total research obligation of $23.6 million—all of 28 percent. By 1966, it had increased to certainly not less than $62.4 million and probably more nearly $78.4 million, amounting to between 53 percent and 63 percent of the total for mathematical-sciences research. Recommendations 6 and 7 essentially call for agencies that traditionally sponsored applied research in the mathematical sciences to continue to do so at levels and in directions in which it has been found useful, and for newly established agencies to contemplate comparable participation in the development, adaptation, and use of mathematical techniques relevant to their problems. No long-term rates of growth are projected, and levels are expected to be set by needs and opportunities as they are identified. The yearly rate of growth of this portion of the research budget has been decreasing, but the latest figures place it still above the growth rate for academic research in comparable periods.

Sources and Forms

Continued participation in the support of academic research by the National Science Foundation and by other agencies is called for by Recommendations 5 and 6. No quantitative apportionment of relative shares is proposed, provided the levels of Recommendations 11 and 12 are met.

Recommendations 8 and 9 identify the relative functions of project funds and other forms of support for academic research. Again trends rather than absolute quantities are stressed. It is proposed that project support remain pre-eminent and, among the various forms of broader support, areas as well as departmental grants be given increased utilization as against interdepartmental and institution-wide grants for the development of quality in the mathematical sciences.

Cautionary Remarks

The mathematical sciences, perhaps more than any other major discipline of modern science, play a pivotal role in a wide variety of contexts, both in opportunities for application and in requirements of education. The programs recommended in our report reflect this diversity. Each of these programs is designed to meet needs that in some contexts have emerged as urgent, but no single priority scale applies across the board; hence their adoption as a whole or in part, down to some given level of priority, cannot be made the subject of a single action at the national level. Instead, we expect our recommendations to be implemented, either individually or jointly, as permitted by the internal priorities of the various agencies involved and by the national emphasis given to the goals of which our objectives are a part. Many of our recommended programs may, of course, be completely merged into other similar but broader programs.

The same considerations apply to our crude projections of costs, with their wide differences in reliability, amounts involved, and periods spanned. To combine them all into one grand balance sheet would not be very useful. Each of the contexts for implementation of these programs has its own scale of benefits relative to which the programs must be weighed.

Since a number of these programs will be funded by agencies that share in their implementation as parts of other, broader activities, often of a more applied nature, a good deal of support of the mathematical sciences may be termed "implicit." In particular, this implies that the federal government must be alert to the impact on the mathematical sciences of abrupt shifts in criteria for support within mission-oriented agencies.

II

The State of the Mathematical Sciences

This part of the report contains an overview of the mathematical sciences. It has been written in a form that we hope will be meaningful to nonmathematicians. In order to accomplish this, and to keep the report within reasonable size, it was necessary to sacrifice any attempt at completeness. It was also necessary to avoid details and the use of symbolism, without which a profound discussion of mathematical subjects may be impossible. Yet we hope that this Part, supplemented by our collection of essays,[7] will communicate to the nonmathematical scientist and the educated layman a feeling for the intellectual atmosphere of mathematical sciences at the threshold of the last third of the twentieth century.

3

The Community of Mathematics

HISTORICAL PERSPECTIVES

Starting with the first expression of rational thought, mathematical thinking influenced the development of our culture in general and was decisive in the creation of science and technology. The invention and development of the infinitesimal calculus preceded the eighteenth century age of enlightenment; these mathematical ideas and techniques made possible the beginning of the industrial age. The many mathematicians engaged in the development of analysis extended the scope of mathematics itself and provided tools for solving problems as diverse as those of the motions of dynamical systems, the flow of liquids and gases, problems involving the strength of materials, and, late in the nineteenth century, the theory of electrical and magnetic phenomena. The definitive formulation of this latter area by Maxwell required still more advanced mathematics. Alongside these developments in analysis, general mathematical ideas in algebra and geometry found their important role in foundations of physical theories. The non-Euclidean geometries and more abstract spaces became the mathematical precursors of new physical theories—the theory of relativity, for example. Certain abstract mathematical constructions constitute a prelude to formulations of quantum theory. By the end of the nineteenth century and at the beginning of the twentieth century a vast mathematical apparatus was being used not only for dealing with problems in astronomy and in physics and in many branches of engineering, but also in sciences like chemistry, which are built upon theories in physics and involve an increasing use of mathematics—on all levels from the elementary to the most abstract.

Because of the long, deep, and essential connection between the growth of mathematics and that of physics, mathematics is often classed with the physical sciences; its impact on civilization until very recently was almost exclusively through its applications to astronomy, physics, chemistry, and engineering. Yet mathematics has features that distinguish it from all experimental sciences—and perhaps from all other sciences.

One is the deep roots that mathematics has in the past. Some of the problems on which mathematicians work today go back several thousand years. Much of contemporary mathematics is a direct continuation of the work begun by the ancient Greeks. A more basic difference between mathematics and experimental sciences, including even the most theoretical branches, lies in the extent to which mathematical research originates within the body of mathematics itself. Physicists, chemists, biologists, and psychologists are more or less directly concerned with observable phenomena. Mathematicians often receive the seed of their problems from the outside world, sometimes through other sciences, but once a mathematical problem or concept has been formulated, it acquires, as it were, a life of its own. In a simplified way mathematics consists of abstractions of real situations, abstractions of abstractions of real situations, and so on. It is surprising but true that these abstractions of abstractions often turn out to further our knowledge and control of the world in which we live.

During and after the Second World War, mathematical thinking penetrated the sciences and the development and organization of technology at an ever-accelerating rate. Probability theory has played an increasing role not only in the natural sciences but increasingly in all work dealing with problems of organization, in economics, and in sociology. In the last decades, problems of life sciences—in biology especially—have begun to require mathematical formulations. Dramatic recent discoveries in molecular biology open still newer prospects for the use of mathematical ideas and models in the understanding of life processes. This increasing rate of mathematization is further accelerated by the development and use of automatic computers.

New fields of technology, made possible through the exploitation of the discoveries in physics of this century, require sophisticated use of mathematics as an absolutely necessary condition. The enormous progress in electronics that has changed the entire pattern of communication—including information theory, network synthesis, feedback theory—would have been unthinkable without all the mathematics that goes into the development of basic concepts and into their application. The technology of nuclear energy and the conquest of space are being made possible only through the advent of the automatic computer, a development which in turn was predicated upon all the work in foundations of mathematics and mathematical logic, along with the technology of electronics.

Mathematics is involved in the problems of communication—through the telephone, the radio, the transmission of pictures—and, more recently, in the exponentially growing problems of collection, classification, and transmission of data in general. Physical communication and transportation, on the ground and especially in the air, require increasingly a study of organization and traffic-control problems of mathematical character. It is no exaggeration to say, therefore, that the fundamental problems of national life depend now, more than ever before, upon the existence and the further growth of the mathematical sciences and upon the continuing activities of able people skilled in their use.

The developments sketched above amount to a mathematization of our culture. The remarkable growth in this mathematization is easily documented. For instance, an authoritative report on applied mathematics submitted to President Roosevelt in 1940[8] estimated that in the future industry might require as many as 10 mathematics PhD's per year. By contrast, the figures of new mathematics PhD's entering industry in 1966 has been estimated at 200. Several new disciplines, like mathematical linguistics, hardly existed 25 years ago. Less dramatic but not less significant is the increase in mathematical sophistication in all fields of engineering.

In all engineering journals, 50 percent or more of the papers in recent issues would probably have been rejected by the editors as too mathematical ten or fifteen years ago.

The preceding lines are from W. Prager's memorandum to COSRIMS. In this same memorandum he writes that:

Twenty years ago, the typical mathematical preparation of the future engineer consisted of a review course in trigonometry and analytic geometry and a formal course in calculus aimed at proficiency in handling routine problems. Today, the review course has disappeared from the curriculum while the emphasis in the second course has shifted from problem solving to the understanding of basic concepts. A fairly rigorous course on ordinary differential equations has been added to the typical curriculum, and students are encouraged to take as many mathematical electives as can be fitted into their program. Foremost among these are vector and tensor analysis, complex variables, transform methods, variational calculus, probability and statistics, and numerical analysis.

Mathematics was, of course, always a traditional part of the education of an engineer. But now it is becoming an essential part of the education of biologists, psychologists, economists, and many others. Therefore, the first obligation the mathematical community has toward society is in the realm of education. We consider these problems in Part III of this report.

Another novel situation is the greatly increased number of people doing mathematical research. Mathematical sciences have shared with all sciences the almost explosive increase in the number of investigators. For instance, *Mathematical Reviews,* an international abstracting journal, reviewed approximately 2,000 papers in 1940 and approximately 15,000 in 1966. The number of mathematical journals published throughout the world has increased correspondingly. These figures in themselves would be of little significance had the increase in quantity been paid for by a drop in quality. While objective studies of quality in mathematical or indeed any research are difficult, it is the considered opinion of this Committee that both the average quality of published research and the quality of the best work today are comparable with what they were in the 1920's or in the decade preceding World War I.

The Nature of Mathematics

The essential features of mathematical search and discovery have remained the same for centuries. So have its main sources of inspiration: the external world and its own internal structure.

Mathematics done for its own sake is traditionally designated as "pure mathematics" and mathematical investigations aimed at increasing our understanding of the world are classified as "applied mathematics." Such a division of mathematics into pure and applied, however, is difficult to maintain; the origin of many important mathematical ideas can be ultimately traced to applications, and, on the other hand, mathematics created for its own sake often turns out to be important for applications.

The mode of origin of a mathematical concept or technique may be only very loosely correlated with its ultimate applications. Fourier considered mathematics as a tool for describing nature. But the impact of "Fourier series," crucially important as these series are in physics and engineering, has been particularly felt in some of the "purest" branches of mathematics. Cayley, on the other hand, believed that matrices, which he invented, would never be applied to anything useful (and was happy about it). They are now an everyday working tool of engineers, physicists, economists, and statisticians.

Geometry originated in practical problems of land measurement. It was developed by the Greeks into an axiomatic system and intensively studied for its own sake. Among Euclid's axioms, there was one (the parallel axiom) that was less intuitively evident than the others. The realization that this axiom could not be logically derived from the remaining ones came only after centuries of struggle and led to the discovery of non-Euclidean geometries (see Coxeter's essay in reference 7). At the time of their birth, these geometries were the answer to a purely logical problem, and even their creators did not dare to attribute to them any counterparts in the real world. But Riemann already suspected that the physical universe in the large may be non-Euclidean, and his intuition was brilliantly confirmed by Einstein's theory of general relativity, a theory that still provides mathematicians with challenging problems.

These examples show the futility of attempting to draw dividing lines between pure and applied mathematics. The difference is not so much in subject matter as in original motivation. Also the name "pure mathematics" is unfortunate since it implies a monastic aloofness from the world at large and an isolation from its scientific, technological, and social concerns. Such an aloofness may be characteristic of some mathematicians. It is certainly not characteristic of mathematics as a collective intellectual endeavor. In fact, many of the greatest mathematicians have attacked, with equal vigor, enjoyment, and success problems posed by nature and problems arising from mathematics itself. For example, Hermann Weyl contributed in equal measure to the theory of groups as a pure mathematical discipline and to the effective uses of this theory in the theoretical constructions of atomic physics.

We, therefore, prefer not to use the term "pure mathematics," but replace it by the more descriptive term "core mathematics." The core comprises those highly developed subdivisions of mathematics that have been and are being investigated primarily for their own sake. The term "core mathematics" also reminds us of the central position of so-called "pure" mathematics with respect to all mathematical sciences.

Intellectual curiosity and intellectual excitement are the main motivating forces behind research in all mathematical sciences, as they are in all sciences in general. The thrill of recognizing a pattern in a seemingly chaotic situation and of reducing a large number of apparently unrelated phenomena to a single simple principle are again characteristic of all sciences; but in the mathematical sciences, and especially in core mathematics, the part played by such considerations is so predominant that some mathematicians consider mathematics to be as much an art as a science.

Mathematics is typically done by individuals rather than by groups; yet it is a collective effort. This is seen, for instance, in the fact that important discoveries are often made by several people working independently in different parts of the world. Personal contact among mathematicians in the same field is often an essential condition for successful work. But the actual work is almost always done by one man thinking about a problem. Very few mathematical papers have three authors and practically none have more. Since mathematics is one of the intellectual activities in which one man—unaided, unsupervised, and undirected—can make important contributions, it continues to attract some of the brightest young people.

One striking feature of mathematical research during the past decade is the confluence of various mathematical disciplines. During the years around World War II the tendency toward specialization appeared serious. It was feared that the boundaries between various fields of core mathematics would solidify so fast that mathematicians of different specialties would be unable to talk to each other. We see now that these fears were not justified. Recent developments have led to an interpenetration of fields, which will be illustrated in Chapter 4.

Indeed many mathematicians believe that this is a golden age of mathematics. They point out that many famous problems that have baffled mathematicians of the past are being solved now, that mathematics is being applied in an ever-increasing number of other disciplines, and that young men entering upon research careers (and their advisers) have no difficulty in identifying interesting problems.

CORE AND APPLICATIONS

"The similarities are essential, but the differences are vital!" Progress in the central core of mathematics proper, where most of the essential tools and new concepts are hammered out, has long and in large measure depended upon abstraction, upon recognizing that seemingly very different things have enough in common to be governed by common considerations, by an abstractly formulated mathematical structure. History shows that the worker in the core accomplishes more if he acts, and often feels, as if things abstractly equivalent were really the same.

In the applied mathematical sciences, however, it is often necessary to take almost the opposite attitude to that which is so helpful in the core. Here the important aspects are specific (sometimes quite concrete, sometimes more abstract from the viewpoint of some particular subject-matter field), rather than mathematically abstract. Indeed, the mathematical abstraction is almost always approximate, and it is usually vital to admit, at the proper time, the approximate character of the answers.

For the applications of mathematics to grow at a rate commensurate with the demands of society, they must continue to receive an ever-growing supply of new results, new concepts, and new approaches from the central core. Applied areas would ultimately starve without what is made available by the core. Less directly and obviously, but just as inevitably, the core would lose much stimulation and implicit guidance, and indeed its development would be badly distorted and stunted, if it were cut off from applications. It is essential to recognize both the existence and complexity of these relations between the core and applied areas and the importance of maintaining communication between them. We shall return to this question.

Those intellectual efforts coming half way between core mathematics, on the one hand, and the sciences and technologies to which mathematics is applied, on the other, are often referred to as "applied mathematics." This is accurate only if it is understood that these efforts include not only the traditional parts of mathematics concerned with applications in physics, chemistry, and engineering (which we shall refer to as physical mathematics or classical applied mathematics), but also statistics, computer science, the general field of optimized allocation, control, and decision-making, and fields such as mathematical biology. Each of these fields has a character of its own, but they have in common a spirit that is well described in reference 9:

> . . . mathematics is "applied" if conceived in a spirit of ready cooperation with sister sciences in the grand endeavor of comprehending our environment, making sense of ourselves, and bringing order into their interaction. Like all good mathematics, good applied mathematics is original and imaginative in the invention and use of its concepts and in its tentative modeling constructions. Its chief distinction from pure mathematics, which shows self-motivated progress along dimly discernible natural paths of growth towards intellectually satisfying goals, lies in adding to this conceptual activity a deep concern for the world of outer experience and a ready interest in problems beyond the confines of mathematics.

In common with the core mathematician, many applied mathematicians are interested in the stimulation of the development of new mathematics—but with primary emphasis on those aspects strongly and directly motivated by scientific, technological, or sociological problems. In common with the theoretical scientist, the applied mathematician seeks knowledge and understanding of facts and phenomena through the use of mathematical methods.

The applied mathematician is most typically engaged in the formulation, analysis, and interpretation of mathematical models: in other words, (a) the formulation of scientific, technological, or practical problems in terms of abstract mathematical models; (b) the solution of the resultant mathematical problems, which may consist of detailed answers or new techniques; and (c) the discussion, interpretation, and evaluation of the results of this analysis, especially in relation to the correspondence between the abstract model and the real world. In different areas of the applied and partly mathematical sciences, the character of these models may be quite different. In computer science, for example, they sometimes take the form of a detailed computer program. The final goal of these efforts is the creation of ideas, concepts, and methods that are of basic significance to the subject in question. As mentioned above, these efforts may lead to the creation of new mathematical ideas and theories.

When thinking of "applications" and "mathematics" together, the nonmathematician tends to think of an immediately applicable solution to his own pressing problem. The applied mathematical sciences do indeed contribute in such immediate ways, but they also contribute throughout a range, of greater or less immediacy, stretching to the very edge of core mathematics. All these varied kinds of contribution are important, not least those that have the same pure-science character as core mathematics.

CRITICISMS AND TENSIONS

The highly exciting achievements within core mathematics and explosive penetration of mathematics into other fields are generally recognized. At the same time, criticism of mathematicians by other scientists as well as criticisms within the mathematical community itself are far from uncommon. Certain of these criticisms may be summarized as follows. It is said that during the recent past mathematicians have alienated themselves from the mainstream of scientific development.

One thing modern mathematicians tend to overlook is that the giants of former days were all actively interested in physics as well as mathematics. This is the first generation for which this is no longer true.
—From a letter by a prominent physicist

It is also claimed that what contemporary pure mathematicians do is of interest only to themselves and most, if not all, of it will never be used in any other discipline. While all sciences require sophisticated mathematical tools and present interesting and challenging mathematical questions, mathematicians are said to be ignorant of and not interested in these questions. This state of affairs is alleged to be particularly and perhaps specifically characteristic of American mathematicians.

Has American mathematics become so remote that scientists will have to turn to other schools of mathematics [Russia?] for help in the future?
—From the same letter by the physicist

This criticism is not new. Mathematicians have long been criticized for being too abstract and too remote from the needs of science. Thus as knowledgeable and distinguished a mathematician as Felix Klein considered the Hamilton-Jacobi theory of dynamics as a plaything of no use for physics (F. Klein, *Vorlesungen über die Entwick-*

lung der Mathematik im 19. Jahrhundert, I, Springer, Berlin, 1926, p. 207). Yet the Hamilton-Jacobi theory proved to be the basis of quantum mechanics. Even the greatest of physicists may err in their evaluation of mathematics. Einstein was at first reluctant to accept Minkowski's four-dimensional geometry as the proper description of special relativity, and several years later he was reluctant to express his physical ideas in the language of tensors. The history of science has shown time and time again that it is impossible to predict what mathematical theories will turn out to be useful outside of pure mathematics.

This point can hardly be stressed too much. Planning the over-all emphasis of mathematics, either for the progress of mathematics as an end in itself or for its application to other sciences and technologies, must fail lamentably. There is a process of natural selection in mathematics. For instance, abstraction for abstraction's sake rots away rapidly if it leads to no new intellectual progress; abstraction that only appears to be for abstraction's sake often proves to be of vital importance. Unconstrained opportunities to succeed or fail; broad diversity, both of individual activities and organizational patterns; ease of change, especially in giving up old patterns—these are the characteristics that have tended to allow the mathematical sciences to make progress.

The claim that "the giants of former days were all actively interested in physics as well as mathematics" is illusory. To be sure, Gauss, Riemann, and Poincaré were actively interested in physics. But one can easily think of first-rank mathematicians of the nineteenth century whose interests were exclusively mathematical. Among them there were several whose work, unbeknown to themselves, turned out to be of vital importance for other sciences (for instance, Frobenius, who founded the theory of group representations). There have been contemporary mathematicians with interests as catholic as those of the greatest men of the nineteenth century—for example, Hermann Weyl, Wiener, and Von Neumann or Gelfand and Kolmogorov—but it is unreasonable to expect more than a few such men in a generation.

Still, the charge that mathematicians have separated themselves from their sister disciplines like physics and astronomy reflects a true state of affairs. Specialization is the inevitable price of the increase of knowledge. One cannot expect many future scientists to combine mathematical and physical achievements in the manner of Newton or Gauss. Yet we must not allow ourselves or our students to become intimidated by the "explosion of knowledge." The problem facing us is mainly that of communication and, by implication, that of education.

IMPROVING COMMUNICATIONS

In the mathematical sciences, as in most other sciences, the explosive growth of activities has had an important side effect. The problems of communication between scientists in various disciplines, between the creators of new theories and the users of these theories, between investigators and teachers, between teachers at various levels, between working scientists and scientific administrators, and last but not least between the scientific community and the citizenry at large have become difficult and require a conscious effort at solutions.

The volume of scientific literature has increased so much that the average working mathematician cannot even scan all the review journals. This results in the paradoxical situation that while many more printed pages of mathematics appear than ever before, mathematicians must depend to a large extent on personal contacts and personal correspondence in order to keep abreast of the current developments in their specialties. (This explains why conferences and symposia are an indispensable part of contemporary scientific research.) The ultimate solution may come from radical new methods for storing, retrieving, and dispensing information. Perhaps journals, books, and libraries as we know them will be replaced by other techniques. This, however, will not happen at once.

A different problem is that of communication between various branches of the mathematical community. Here the difficulties are not technical but psychological and intellectual. In the central area of core mathematics any threat to the exchange of ideas and results between subdisciplines has been overcome through recent unifying tendencies. On the other hand, this danger is acute as far as the interfaces between core mathematics and the applied and partly mathematical sciences are concerned and even more so between the mathematical sciences as a whole and the various users of mathematics. What is needed is a conscious effort by highly qualified people to overcome this "communication gap" by specially written books and articles, by interdisciplinary conferences and courses, and by other appropriate means. If this endeavor is to be successful, leadership must come from the profession, specifically from individuals. Financial support, where necessary, will also have to be found.

The problems of communication and publication have recently been considered in more detail by the American Mathematical Society's *ad hoc* Committee on Information Exchange and Publication in Mathematics. By special permission we have reproduced that committee's final report in Appendix B. Its recommendations are addressed to the American Mathematical Society but may provide more general guidance.

During the past decade, the mathematical sciences have made strenuous and successful efforts to establish communications between the investigators and teachers of mathematics at various levels. The various programs for curriculum reform in high schools and elementary schools involve joint work by university mathematicians and teachers. The manifold activities of the Committee on the Undergraduate Program in Mathematics (CUPM) establish a link between graduate schools and colleges. We do not believe that any of these groups has already found definitive solutions to the problems of mathematics education. Valuable steps have already been taken, however, and such work should be continued and supported.

The problem of making mathematics understandable to the educated layman continues to be almost insurmountable. A Greek tyrant who wanted a rapid explanation of mathematics was told that there was no royal road to this science. This remains true. It is equally true, however, that the mathematical community has a duty to do all it can to make its work understandable to those who want to understand it. The collection of essays[7] to be published in conjunction with our report is a modest contribution in this direction.

4

Core Mathematics

A "state-of-the-art" report for core mathematics will not be attempted here. It would be almost impossible to prepare a report meaningful to nonmathematicians, and a report of value to the mathematical community would require an extraordinary effort by a very large number of people. Instead we attempt in this chapter to describe in rather general terms some aspects of core mathematics as it appears to some of its practitioners. The essays on selected topics in mathematics, which appear in a separate volume,[7] serve as an elaboration and illustration.

We organize our remarks around the traditional subdivisions of core mathematics. It should be remembered, however, that the boundaries between these fields have become much less precise than they used to be, and that some of the most important developments are occurring precisely at the interfaces between different fields or in areas that cannot be accommodated within the existing classification. As a matter of fact, the confluence of mathematical ideas and the interpenetration of the various fields are the most characteristic and most rewarding features of contemporary core mathematics. A sketchy presentation couched in nontechnical language can convey only a pale reflection of the excitement felt by those who participate in these developments.

MATHEMATICAL LOGIC

Logic is one of the most ancient mathematical sciences, since it is at least as old as Aristotelian philosophy and Euclidean geometry.

57

However, mathematical logic, also called symbolic logic, really developed in the second half of the ninteenth century, when it was observed that familiar logical operations can be expressed by algebraic formulas, and when it seemed possible to define such basic mathematical concepts as the natural numbers 0, 1, 2, 3, . . . in purely logical terms.

A major reason for the flowering of mathematical logic lies in the creation of the theory of infinite sets, during the same period, by Georg Cantor. This theory influenced all mathematics. It also led to the discovery of paradoxes, nonsensical conclusions reached by seemingly legitimate reasoning processes. Some of these new paradoxes* are similar to ones encountered by ancient Greek philosophers,† which Aristotle disposed of by what we now consider insufficient arguments.

Since unfettered reasoning had led to paradoxes, mathematicians recognized that the processes of logical thought require regulation. Thus, it should be possible to reduce any legitimate piece of mathematical reasoning to manipulation of symbols using only stated axioms and stated rules of inference. So reduced, the reasoning is said to be "formalized." Of course, formalization in itself provides no warranty that paradoxes will not arise (as indeed they might if the axioms and rules have been badly chosen). But without formalization we cannot deal in a precise way with the problem of suitably regulating mathematics.

For many years it was the hope of mathematicians that all mathematical reasoning could be formalized in one logical system. A remarkable discovery by Gödel in 1931 shattered this hope, however, and had far-reaching repercussions among the philosophers. What Gödel established was "incompleteness" for certain particular formal systems ("Principia Mathematica" of Whitehead and Russell, and related systems). But the incompleteness was soon recognized as applying to every formal system that is correct (only true statements being provable) and sufficiently rich to include ordinary arithmetic. In any such system, there are statements, even about whole numbers, that are true but cannot be proved within the system.

---

* Here is a sample. The expression, "the least natural number not nameable in fewer than twenty-two syllables," names in twenty-one syllables a natural number which by its definition cannot be named in fewer than twenty-two syllables. (G. G. Berry, 1906)

† X says, "I am lying." Is X telling the truth? (Eubulides, fourth century B.C.)

This generalized form of Gödel's theorem rests on accepting a precise analysis of what an "algorithm" or "preassigned computational procedure" is in general. Such an analysis, accepted by most logicians, was given in 1936 by Church and independently (in an equivalent form) by Turing. Previously, mathematicians had dealt only with many particular examples of algorithms, some discovered by Euclid or before.

Church and Turing each used their analysis to exhibit an infinite class of questions with the property that no algorithm suffices to answer correctly all the questions of the class. No matter how long and hard mathematicians may have worked at devising methods for answering questions of the class, there will be some questions that can be answered only by inventing still further methods. Most recently (since 1948), it has been shown that such classes of questions (sometimes called "unsolvable problems") arise in other parts of mathematics.

One of Cantor's first achievements was the proof that there are "more" points on a straight line than there are natural numbers; it is impossible to match up all the points on a line with the natural numbers 0, 1, 2, 3, ... Cantor conjectured that any set of points on the line either can be rearranged into a simple sequence or else contains "as many" points as there are on the whole line. This conjecture, called the continuum hypothesis, was considered one of the main unsolved problems in mathematics. In 1939, Gödel proved that the continuum hypothesis cannot be *disproved* by the methods used in contemporary mathematics and formalized in existing systems of set theory. About a quarter of a century later, P. Cohen showed that the continuum hypothesis cannot be *proved* by such methods either. For further information see Smullyan's essay in reference 7.

What has been said up to now may convey the impression that mathematical logic is a highly abstract subject, related to philosophy and much too esoteric even for the taste of most mathematicians. This is indeed the case. Yet this most austere of all mathematical disciplines has made a contribution to America's fastest-growing industry. By reducing mathematical reasoning, and in fact all deductive reasoning, to purely mechanical manipulation of symbols according to definite rules, mathematical logic prepared for the development of digital computers. Indeed, a mathematical theory has been completely formalized if any argument in it could in principle be checked by computer. It is no accident that two mathematicians (Von Neumann and Turing) steeped in mathematical logic participated in the development of modern computers. The recognition, by Von Neumann, that Turing's work implies the possibility of a universal computer saved years and millions of dollars in development.

The interplay between mathematical logic and computing continues. Training in mathematical logic is often a way to creative work in computer sciences, and the problems on which computer scientists and logicians work sometimes have certain features in common. Logicians, for instance, are interested to know whether certain problems can be solved by algorithms. Computer scientists ask the same question, except that they want to know whether certain problems can be solved by algorithms in a reasonable time on existing or projected machines, and, if so, how this can be done in the most economical way.

The difficulties in the foundations of mathematics that led to the development of mathematical logic have not yet been wholly resolved. There are various schools and points of view. For example, in formulating existence proofs one school, the constructivists, recognizes as valid only proofs in terms of algorithms, while another school, the formalists, will accept a proof by contradiction.

NUMBER THEORY

Number theory is perhaps the oldest mathematical discipline. Positive integers appear to have been invented along with language, and the most ancient civilizations that left written records were fascinated by properties of integers. Problems in the theory of numbers can often be stated in a surprisingly simple manner, understandable to every schoolboy. Many of them deal with prime numbers, those integers greater than 1 that are divisible only by themselves and by 1 (2, 3, 5, 7, 11, 13, 17, 19, 23, 29, 31, 37, . . .). Here is a famous problem: Is every positive even integer a sum of two primes? The evidence seems to be all for it, as was first observed by Goldbach in the early eighteenth century. Yet the Goldbach problem is unsolved. It has been proved only that every integer is the sum of, at most, 19 primes, and that there is a large number such that every odd integer exceeding it is the sum of three primes.

The fascination that number theory exerts on mathematics is twofold. First, there is the deep though seldom-verbalized conviction that in studying natural numbers we are investigating something imperishable and eternal. We cannot conceive of intelligent thought anywhere in the universe that would not arrive at natural numbers as we know them, and an unshakable evidence of an extraterrestial intelligence would be a communication containing the sequence 2, 3, 5, 7, 11, ...

Another reason for the fascination of number theory is that its problems, simple as they sound, often require for their solution the most elaborate and sophisticated techniques available to mathematics. A characteristic phenomenon of recent decades is the application of probability theory to number theory and, very recently, the applications of mathematical logic.

Modern number theory is concerned not only with integers but also with so-called algebraic integers, that is, with numbers that can be roots of algebraic equations with integer coefficients and highest coefficient 1.* In studying algebraic integers one often uses a geometric language hardly distinguishable from that of algebraic geometry (see below).

Number theory has always had an experimental aspect. Interesting properties of numbers can be discovered by experimentation, though the truth of a proposition about infinitely many numbers can never be established by verifying individual instances, however many. The celebrated prime-number theorem, for instance, asserts that the number of primes between 2 and a larger number x is approximately

$$\frac{x}{1 + \dfrac{1}{2} + \dfrac{1}{3} + \dfrac{1}{4} + \cdots + \dfrac{1}{x}}.$$

This was perceived by Gauss, who had computed long tables of primes. The proof came much later and required, in its original form, arguments from the theory of functions of complex variables.

Its experimental aspect is one reason why number theory is among those disciplines of pure mathematics that feel the impact of the computer revolution. The computer opened up new possibilities for numerical experimentation. Number theorists use computers not only to guess theorems but also to establish results. Numerous plausible conjectures have been refuted by computer work, and

---

* For instance, $1 - \sqrt{2}$ and $1 + \sqrt{2}$ are algebraic integers since both numbers are roots of the equation $x^2 - 2x - 1 = 0$.

D. H. Lehmer used computers to prove theorems requiring too great a ramification into cases for conventional methods of proof.

COMBINATORIAL ANALYSIS

Combinatorial analysis is concerned with a variety of "combinatorial" problems, many of which amount to: "In how many ways can one perform a certain task?" The problems are usually easy to state and may be very difficult to solve. They often have important consequences for physical theory. We give an example:

Consider a checkerboard with n squares on each side, where n is an even number. We ask for the number N_n of different ways in which the board can be covered by dominoes, a domino covering two squares. A complete solution to this problem is not known at the present time; but it was recently found that, for large n, N_n is equal to $(1.338515 \ldots)^{(n^2)}$. This result has significant implications for statistical mechanics.

One of the most famous unsolved problems of mathematics, the four-color problem, is combinatorial. This conjecture states that any planar map can be colored with four colors in such a way that any two adjacent countries have different colors. In spite of the vigorous efforts of many talented mathematicians, this conjecture has not yet been settled; a relatively easy proof shows that five colors suffice.

Many of the developments of modern science and technology are stimulating a renewed interest in combinatorial analysis. Problems are arising from genetics, biochemistry, statistics, coding of information transmitted to and from orbiting satellites, efforts to design efficient circuits for electronic computers, and the development of programming languages. (See Rota's essay in reference 7.)

ALGEBRA

The three major traditional subdivisions of mathematics are algebra, analysis, and geometry. Most people, upon hearing the word "algebra," remember the subject studied in high school and think of problems involving the solution of linear and quadratic equations. Those parts of algebra are actually 4,000 years old, and the language of algebra, that is, the use of variables (letters) to represent numbers, dates from the Renaissance. Modern algebra is largely a development of the last 40 years. Yet its roots go back to earlier times. Some of the essential ideas, for instance, appeared about 1830 in the work of Evariste Galois, a man who was persecuted by his government for his radicalism and by his teachers for his impertinence and who was killed in a duel at the age of 21. Modern algebra began to blossom and to reach maturity as a result of the efforts of a number of algebraists both in this country and abroad, inspired in part by the work of a brilliant woman mathematician, Emmy Noether. Its techniques and mode of thought play an important role not only in other mathematical disciplines but also in various areas of the biological, physical, and social sciences.

Modern algebra is concerned with the study of so-called "algebraic structures." Most of these may be considered as generalizations of the basic structures of elementary mathematics: the system of integers, the system of rational numbers, the system of real numbers, the system of complex numbers, and the system of vectors (arrows) in space.

We begin with an example of a structure. The elements in the system of rational numbers are positive and negative common fractions and integers, and the number 0. Among these elements there are defined two operations, addition and multiplication. Any set of elements for which two operations, called addition and multiplication, are defined, obeying the same formal rules as in the case of rational numbers, is called a field. For instance, the real numbers form a field and so do complex numbers. Galois discovered the existence of finite fields, that is, fields with only finite numbers of elements. For instance, if p is a prime number, there is a field Z_p consisting of p elements, the numbers $0, 1, 2, \ldots, p-1$. Addition and multiplication in this field are defined by the prescription: add and multiply in the usual way, then divide by p; the remainder is called the sum or the product. (For instance, in Z_3 we have $1 + 1 = 2, 1 + 2 = 0, 2 + 2 = 1, 2 \times 2 = 1$.) There are many other fields; for instance, all rational functions of one variable with complex coefficients form a field.

The advantage of considering systems about which we assume nothing except the laws of addition and multiplication is that any statement proved about them applies immediately to a wide variety of fields in various branches of mathematics. The same is true about other algebraic structures. In each case the central problem is to describe the structure of the general system in terms of the structure of particular examples of the system.

We will review briefly some of the subdivisions of modern algebra.

Field Theory

The definition of a field was given above. The modern theory of fields is concerned with the properties of a field K formed from a field F by adjoining to it the roots of polynomial equations with coefficients in F. This theory, the modern development of Galois' original work, is one of the most developed and fruitful parts of algebra.

Ring Theory

A ring is a set of elements in which two operations, addition and multiplication, are defined, and these operations satisfy the same conditions as in a field, with two important exceptions: it is not required that division by an element distinct from 0 be always possible, and it is permitted that the product of two elements depend on the order in which we multiply them. (The latter means that, in a ring, ab and ba may be different.)

An example of a ring is the ring of all integers. Here division is not always possible, but the product of two elements is independent of their order. Such a ring is called commutative. Another example is the ring of all matrices with n rows and n columns. This is a noncommutative ring since, if a and b are two matrices, it may happen that ab and ba are different.

Rings arise naturally in many areas of mathematics. In analysis (see below) many common sets of functions form rings, and the results of ring theory contribute useful theorems in analysis.

Linear Algebra

During the nineteenth century, the theory of systems of linear algebraic equations was codified into so-called linear algebra. This part of algebra probably has more applications in other disciplines, including engineering, physics, statistics, numerical analysis, and social sciences, than any other. It is convenient to clothe linear algebra in a geometric language. The basic concept is that of a vector space over a field.

The standard example of a vector space is the set of ordinary geometric vectors, as used in physics. The elements may be thought of as arrows in ordinary space drawn from a fixed point. Two vectors can be added by the "parallelogram law." A vector can be multiplied by a real number: the product of a vector by a positive number a is obtained by leaving the direction of the vector unchanged and multiplying the length of the vector by a; the product of a vector by a negative number $-a$ is obtained by reversing the direction of the vector and multiplying the length by a; the product of a vector by 0, finally, is the so-called null vector of length 0. This vector space is said to be "over the real numbers," since vectors are multiplied by real numbers.

A vector space over a field F is a set of elements called vectors for which one has defined two operations: addition of two vectors and multiplication of a vector by an element F. It is required that the same formal rules should hold as in the example above.

A vector space over F is said to have dimension n if, roughly speaking, a vector can be specified by giving n elements of F. The space of geometric vectors, for instance, has dimension 3 since, if we introduce a coordinate system, each geometric vector can be expressed by three real numbers. Finite dimensional vector spaces occur in many parts of engineering, physics, statistics, numerical analysis, and the social sciences.

Linear algebra is the study of finite dimensional vector spaces. It is particularly concerned with linear transformation, those mappings of a vector space into itself that preserve addition and multiplication. Any linear transformation can be represented by a matrix (square array of numbers, or of elements of F), so that matrix algebra can be used to study the theory of linear transformations. The results of linear algebra that do not depend on the finite dimension of the vector space have had wide applications in functional analysis (see below).

Algebras

An associative algebra is a finite dimensional vector space which is also a ring. The study of such algebras began with the quaternions of Hamilton (1843). The first definitive results were the fundamental structure theorems proved by Wedderburn in 1907. In recent years, these results have been subsumed in results on the structure of rings. An associative algebra is called a division algebra if division by nonzero elements is always possible. Division algebras are the building blocks in the theory of algebras. Their structure has been extensively studied, but a complete structure theory has not yet been given.

A nonassociative algebra is a structure obeying the same rules as an algebra, except that the product of three elements may depend upon which two one multiplies first. Two classes of such algebras are of main importance. The first are Lie algebras, in which any three elements x,y,z satisfy the identity $xy + yx = x(yz) + y(zx) + z(xy) = 0$. Such algebras are fundamental for the study of continuous groups and, in recent years, have played an important role in theoretical physics. The second class is that of the Jordan algebras, originally suggested by quantum physics. These are characterized by the identities $xy - yx = x(yx^2) - (xy)x^2 = 0$.

Group Theory

Groups are among the simplest and most important algebraic structures. One of the most elementary examples of a group is the set of all positive rational numbers in which one considers only the operation of multiplication. A group is a set of elements in which one operation, called group operation or group multiplication, is defined; this operation must obey the same formal rules as ordinary multiplication of rational numbers, except that we do not require the commutative law (that is, ab and ba need not be the same). The integers form a group if the group operation is the ordinary addition; this group is infinite (it contains infinitely many elements) and commutative. A somewhat more complicated example is the finite group S_n consisting of all permutations of the first n integers. The group composition of two permutations is obtained by carrying out the first permutation and following it by the second. If n is greater than 2, S_n is not commutative.

A basic problem of group theory is to determine the structure of all finite groups. Since the building blocks out of which all finite groups are constructed are the so-called finite "simple" groups,* an

* We give, for the sake of completeness, the precise definition of a "simple" group. Let G and H be finite groups and let f be a rule that assigns to every element g of G an element $h = f(g)$ of H. If this rule preserves the group operation, that is, if $f(g_1 g_2) = f(g_1) f(g_2)$, and if every element of H is assigned to some element of G, then f is called a homomorphism of G onto H. The group G is "simple" if every homomorphism is either a homomorphism onto a group H having as many elements as G or a homomorphism onto a group G consisting of a single element.

important part of the problem is the determination of the structure of these groups. There has been a recent breakthrough in the
subject with the proof (by Thompson and Feit) that if the number
of elements in a finite simple group is not a prime, it must be even.
This result has already had far-reaching implications and lends
strong support to the hope that in the not too distant future the
structure of all finite simple groups will be explicitly determined.

Groups are of fundamental importance in many mathematical
investigations and in many applications of mathematics. Some
people believe the underlying reason for this is that groups give a
precise mathematical meaning to the important geometric concept
of symmetry. (A brilliant exposition of this point of view is found
in Hermann Weyl's book.[10])

Galois used finite groups to study the solvability of algebraic
equations by radicals, that is, by formulas involving only arithmetic
operations and root extractions. He showed that an equation can
be so solved only if its roots exhibit a certain symmetry. This
symmetry is always present in equations of degree 2, 3, and 4 but
not, in general, in equations of higher degree. In particular, there
is no general formula, involving radicals, for solving a fifth-degree
equation. (This epoch-making result was established before Galois
by Abel, another mathematical genius who died at an early age.)

The theory of groups is of importance in chemistry and physics.
The theory of finite groups has applications in crystallography, in
the theory of inorganic complex ions, and in spectroscopy. During
the 1920's and 1930's infinite groups were used in quantum
mechanics. Recent developments at the forefront of physics research
are intimately tied with the concept of symmetry and hence with
groups. As a matter of fact, physicists now use quite sophisticated
results from group theory. For more details, see Dyson's essay in
reference 7.

Homological Algebra and Category Theory

Modern mathematics is characterized by an ever-increasing range of
applications of algebra to other mathematical subjects (see Eilenberg's essay in reference 7). A particularly striking example is
topology, a branch of geometry concerned with qualitative rather
than quantitative aspects of shapes of geometric figures. In the early
1920's it was recognized, under the influence of Emmy Noether
especially, that the methods used by topologists are basically alge-

braic. But just as every science that uses mathematics not only exploits the existing mathematical theories but reshapes them to its own needs, so topologists developed algebraic tools suitable for their needs. The next step was a return to pure algebra. Algebraic methods created for the needs of topology have been analyzed, codified, and studied for their own sake. This led to two new subdivisions in algebra: category theory and homological algebra. These are perhaps the most abstract specialities in algebra. Categories provide a language for discussing *all* algebraic systems of a given type. The result is, as is so often the case in mathematics, a wide variety of applications to diverse mathematical fields, in this case from logic to such "applied" areas as the theory of automata.

ANALYSIS

Analysis, the youngest of the three traditional divisions of mathematics, consists of ramifications of the calculus, a subject that was discovered in the seventeenth century. The invention of the calculus, traditionally associated with the names of Newton and Leibnitz, was a momentous event in human history that made possible modern physical science.

The gist of the intellectual revolution brought about by the calculus may be described as follows. If one wants to study by means of calculus a complicated process occurring in nature, or in a machine, or in society, or in a purely ideal mathematical world, one begins by analyzing what happens "in the small." "In the small" may mean during a very short time interval, or over a very small area, or for very small changes of some other quantity. In many cases it is relatively easy to find out how various interdependent quantities change in the small. Formulas expressing this are usually differential equations. The second task consists of deriving from the simple laws governing what happens in the small the incomparably more complicated laws describing what happens in the large. This second step usually involves solving differential equations—a purely mathematical task.

Solving differential equations may have a different meaning depending on the circumstances. Sometimes one is able to write down a formula for a solution. More often one can only prove that there is a solution satisfying the desired conditions, and one can indicate a method for computing this solution approximately. Neither of the two procedures may give all desired answers, since one often wants to know how the solution depends upon the various quantities entering into the problem and what happens when some of these become very large.

Here is an example going back to Newton. The motion of our planetary system during a very short time interval may be described as follows. Every celestial body is moving toward every other celestial body with an acceleration directly proportional to the mass of the other body and inversely proportional to the square of its distance from that other body. To calculate on the basis of the instantaneous behavior of the planets and their satellites their actual motion means to solve the differential equations of celestial mechanics. Generations of mathematicians have developed efficient methods for this. Today the job can be done, with comparative ease, by using modern computers. However, the computers cannot tell us whether the solar system will preserve its general shape in the distant future. To discuss this stability problem requires new theoretical investigations. We add that such stability questions are not at all as devoid of practical importance as they seem at first glance (see page 73, second paragraph).

Since the creation of the calculus, analysis has penetrated practically all parts of mathematics, both because of its intrinsic richness and because of its manifold applications. Its subdivisions acquired lives of their own and are often pursued for their own sake. Experience shows, however, that the theory of differential equations almost always utilizes the methods and ideas developed in the seemingly remote parts of analysis, as well as in other branches of mathematics. We shall mention briefly some disciplines in analysis that are presently active and in which important results have recently been achieved.

Functions of Complex Variables

It has long been recognized that certain parts of the calculus become understandable and harmonious only if one extends the system of ordinary "real" numbers to include "imaginary" and "complex" numbers. For instance, this extension unifies the theories of elementary functions like trigonometric functions, logarithms, and exponentials. Complex analysis is the theory of analytic functions of complex variables. These are functions that can be represented by certain infinite series (power series). As an independent discipline, the theory of analytic functions developed from the work of Cauchy, Riemann, and Weierstrass during the nineteenth century. Riemann's work used physical and geometrical imagery, yet it came as a surprise to many scientists that complex analysis proved such a useful discipline for so many other fields of knowledge (electrical engineering, fluid dynamics, and so on). In recent years, the concept of analytic functions has proved useful at the very foundation of high-energy physics. (See Wightman's article in reference 7.)

Complex analysis illustrates the earlier statement about confluence of fields. Several decades ago, complex function theory was a flourishing field but with rigidly circumscribed boundaries. Mathematicians working in this field communicated primarily among themselves, and most of their work was of limited interest to other mathematicians. Today, however, many experts in complex analysis use tools from topology, geometry, and algebra, and their work in turn is of interest to an ever-widening circle of other mathematicians. This is especially true of the work in the theory of functions of several complex variables, which has flourished during the past two decades. (For fuller treatment of functions of complex variables, see Bers' essay in reference 7.)

Harmonic Analysis

Harmonic analysis may be described as that part of analysis that originated from the study of vibrating strings. In the eighteenth century, Bernoulli tried to represent the motion of a vibrating string as a superposition of so-called simple harmonic motions, that is, motions described by trigonometric sine functions. The same idea was used by Fourier in studying heat conduction, and the resulting superpositions have come to be known as Fourier series. Just as the sound produced by a musical instrument can be analyzed into a superposition of pure tones, so physicists can describe many complicated processes and states as a superposition of eigenfunctions—solutions of differential equations corresponding in some sense to pure tones. The mathematics of such a representation provides one of the basic tools for solving the differential equations of mathematical physics and has been a source of interesting and difficult problems for generations of workers in pure mathematics. This work and its generalizations comprise the field of harmonic analysis.

Another direction of research originating from the problem posed by Bernoulli consisted in refinement rather than in generalization. Bernoulli asserted in effect that any function can be represented by a Fourier series. The statement produced many controversies and, in particular, led to the clarification of the concept of function, to the first rigorous definition of the basic concept of integral, by Riemann himself, and half a century later to the extension of this concept by Lebesgue. A highly technical question in the theory of Fourier series led Georg Cantor to the notion of set theory. The very recent generalization of the concept of function, Schwartz's distribution theory (see below), was also motivated at least in part by the theory of Fourier series.

For all this manifold activity, the simplest and most naïve formulation of Bernoulli's question remained open until 1965. The precise formulation is necessarily technical: Does a Fourier series of every function converge almost everywhere? The Russian mathematician Kolmogorov showed many years ago that the answer is no, if one admits all functions for which a Fourier series can be formed, by the classical rules. But only recently did Carleson prove that the answer is yes, if the function is continuous (and even under certain weaker hypotheses). This is one of many examples of old and famous problems recently solved.

Functional Analysis

In this century, a new form of analysis has been developed in which the functions of classical analysis are considered as points in a function space and a geometric language is used. (See Schwartz's and McShane's essays in reference 7.) The best-known example is that of Hilbert space, which may be thought of as a space of functions but can also be described as a space with infinitely many coordinates in which distance is given by a formula analogous to the one used in analytic geometry.

The principal objects of study are the so-called operators, which are mappings of one function space into another. Problems in functional analysis often arise from integral equations, differential equations, and other parts of so-called classical analysis.

An important application of functional analysis, or more specifically of Hilbert space, occurs in modern physics. Quantum mechanics is, in fact, entirely based on the concept of Hilbert space. This was first recognized at the very beginning of the theory. At that time, Schrödinger and Heisenberg proposed two apparently different mathematical descriptions of the experimental observations. It turned out that their two descriptions were simply two models of equivalent operators in an abstract Hilbert space. When one compares the multitude of complex, comprehensive, and accurate predications of quantum mechanics, in remarkable agreement with experimental observations, with the highly abstract mathematical concepts, initiated and developed originally for their mathematical appeal alone but utilized later as the language of physics, one never ceases to marvel at the power and the relevance of mathematical abstractions.

Functional analysis is a very active field of research. Examples of recent developments include the theory of representations, the problem of approximations, and the use of topological methods.

Differential Equations

This part of analysis, which, among other things, pervades sizable portions of mathematical physics and classical applied mathematics, has been undergoing a process of almost explosive development during the past decades. No report short of a handbook can do justice to all developments; here we mention only a few highlights and also indicate some of the many uses of differential equations in applied fields.

Differential equations are divided into ordinary and partial. In an ordinary differential equation the unknown is a function, or a system of functions, of a single independent variable. In most applications this variable is time. In a partial differential equation the unknown function, or the unknown functions, depends on several variables. In applications these variables are usually coordinates of a point in space, although one of them may be time. In geometric language, to solve an ordinary differential equation means to find a curve satisfying certain conditions; to solve a partial differential equation means to find a surface or a higher dimensional manifold satisfying certain conditions.

Differential equations are either linear or nonlinear. Instead of giving a formal definition, we describe how such equations arise in applications. Linear equations correspond to situations in which the response of the system studied is proportional to the stimulus. Thus the equations of linear elasticity describe a material in which the deformations are proportional to the forces applied (Hooke's law). A nonlinear equation describes a system for which the response depends on the stimulus in an arbitrary way. In many applications one develops a linear theory as a first approximation, and one is then forced to proceed to a nonlinear theory. For instance, differential equations describing the propagation of small disturbances in air density (sound waves) are linear, while the equations describing the propagation of strong waves are nonlinear. From the mathematical point of view, the linear theory is always simpler.

The modern theory of ordinary differential equations includes control theory, which is closely related to technical and engineering applications. The fundamental problem is to control a system, such as a satellite, by means of certain control mechanisms. It is often desired to bring the system into a certain state (for example, to guide a missile to a target) with a minimum amount of some quantity (such as fuel). This is a problem in "Optimal Control Theory." Although control theory has developed mainly during the past ten years, it has attracted many research workers in both mathematics and engineering; there have been over 400 publications in this field, including a number of books. This is a field to which the Russians, led by Pontryagin, originally a topologist, have contributed a great deal.

One of the more classical developments in ordinary differential equations is stability theory, on which much pioneering work was done many years ago by Poincaré and Birkhoff. Many of the problems raised by them have recently been solved by mathematicians in Russia (Kolmogorov, Arnold) and in this country (Moser). Although the problem has its origin in astronomy (stability of planetary orbits), the methods developed for its solution have applications to high-energy-accelerator design and to the study of charged particles in magnetic fields, like that of the earth. A typical problem is to ensure the containment of charged particles for long times in the narrow tubular vacuum chambers of an accelerator without hitting the wall. Some of the results of these studies have been applied to the orbit theory of artificial satellites near the oblate earth.

Of all the subfields of ordinary differential equations, the theory of structural stability of vector fields (systems of differential equations) on manifolds (i.e., surfaces and their generalization to higher dimensions) is perhaps of interest to the greatest number of mathematicians in other fields. A vector field is said to be structurally stable if the general shape of the solution curves remains unchanged if the vector field is perturbed slightly. In 1959, all structurally stable systems on ordinary surfaces were classified, and it was proved that any vector field on such a manifold can be approximated arbitrarily closely by a structurally stable one. But Smale showed that this approximation theorem is not true on manifolds of dimension greater than three. Whether it holds on manifolds of dimension three is unknown at present. It is hoped that continued work will lead to a general theory of the classification of vector fields.

The recent theory of linear partial differential equations profited from the creation of a new language, the language of "distributions" or generalized functions introduced by L. Schwartz. An example of a distribution is the famous delta function, $\delta(x)$, of Dirac, which takes on the value 0 for all values of $x \neq 0$, but is such that

$$\int_{-\infty}^{+\infty} \delta(x)dx = 1.$$

Mathematicians originally did not recognize this as a legitimate function, but in the late 1940's Schwartz developed a theory of generalized functions, or distributions, in which not only the Dirac function but also much weirder entities occupy a legitimate place. A new generation of mathematicians learned to look at partial differential equations from the viewpoint of distributions, and they have created a new branch of this old discipline that abounds in beautiful and powerful results. Here is an example. *Every* linear partial differential equation with *constant* coefficients, of the form $Lu = f$, where f is any function or generalized function, has solutions (Ehrenpreis-Malgrange). This theorem cannot be generalized any further. If the equation does not have constant coefficients, a solution need not exist. In fact, a few years ago, the experts were surprised by Hans Lewy's discovery of a simple linear partial differential equation that has no solution whatsoever.

Why was this surprising? Because traditionally mathematicians took their partial differential equations from physics, and the existence of the solution was more or less assured by so-called physical intuition. The task of the mathematician was to justify the intuition by a rigorous proof and to produce a method for actually finding the solution. This work is certainly nearing completion as far as linear problems are concerned.

But nature is not always linear. Compressible fluid flow, viscous flow, magnetohydrodynamics and plasma physics, general relativity and other disciplines challenge the mathematicians to solve non-linear problems. The theory of nonlinear partial differential equations is at present a very active discipline. Important break-throughs have been achieved, but an immense amount of work remains to be done.

Much of the modern work in partial differential equations looks highly esoteric, and only a few years ago such work would have been considered of no interest for applications, where one wants a solution expressed in a workable form, say by a sufficiently simple formula. The advent of the modern computing machines has changed this. If a problem involving a differential equation is sufficiently understood theoretically, then, in principle at least, a numerical solution can be obtained on a machine. If the mathematics of the problem is not understood, then the biggest machine and an unlimited number of machine-hours may fail to yield a solution.

Another example from the theory of partial differential equations is the index theorem. Suppose we want to solve a linear equation

$$Lu = f,$$

where L stands for a complicated operator that may involve differentiations, integrations, etc., u is the unknown, which may be a set of numbers, a function, or a set of functions, and f consists of given data. In general, there will be a solution only if f satisfies a certain number of conditions. Let us assume that this number is finite, and let us call it A. Also, if the problem is solvable at all, the solution may not be unique; let us assume that the solution depends on B parameters. The number $A-B$ is called the index of the problem.

The simplest example is a system of n linear algebraic equations in m unknowns. It can easily be shown that in this case the index $A-B$ is equal to $n-m$. The index problem makes sense also when the equations are differential equations, but until very recently it could be solved only in relatively simple cases. This difficult problem was generalized, attacked, and solved about three years ago by Atiyah and Singer. The resulting formula expresses the difference $A-B$ in terms of certain topological invariants of the region and of the equations considered. The work involved not only some of the most refined recent tools of analysis but also results and methods from differential geometry and topology. It also turned out that this index formula contained as special cases several important results in other fields of mathematics and their generalizations. It is completely impossible to assign this beautiful achievement to any one mathematical discipline. It belongs to analysis as much as to geometry and topology, and it has strong connections with algebra.

Probability Theory

The theory of probability, which arose during the sixteenth and seventeenth centuries out of rather frivolous questions of computing odds in gambling, has had an explosive development during the past few decades. On the one hand, this theory, which deals with "mathematics of chance," has been put on firm foundations, which makes it into a science as deductive and as rigorous as geometry and algebra. On the other hand, its range of applications has grown immensely. (See Kac's essay in reference 7 for an extended discussion of probability theory.)

Some 40 years ago the calculus of probability consisted essentially of a collection of disconnected problems. Under the influence of Gauss, undue importance was attached to the so-called theory of errors, a topic now practically forgotten. Instead, probability has moved in new directions by developing the theory of stochastic processes and the modern fluctuation theory. The unexpected results of these theories have introduced entirely new viewpoints and attitudes and have also opened new avenues of research. However, for the purposes of this report it is more important to stress that these developments have broken the traditional isolation of probability theory, with the result that it now plays an important role in a surprising number of mathematical disciplines. Examples of these disciplines are measure theory, function spaces, classical potential theory, Hilbert spaces, information theory, and partial differential equations. This list could be extended, but it should suffice to add that probabilistic methods have been used for proofs in logic. Some recent work promises to establish further new connections between logic and probability.

The same intense and fruitful flow of ideas can be observed between mathematical probability and various applications. Important parts of probability theory were stimulated by technological problems (information and prediction theory, theory of noise), and modern probability is playing an important role in industry and in quality control and reliability engineering, as well as in natural and social sciences. In addition, probability forms the basis of the modern theory of statistical inference (see Kiefer's essay in reference 7).

GEOMETRY

Three turning points in the history of geometry determined the course of mathematics and exerted influences beyond the boundaries of mathematics and even of science in general. The first occurred in Greece, when the collection of geometric facts and rules assembled in the ancient civilizations of the East was transformed into a deductive science. This event signified the birth of deductive reasoning. The second event was the discovery of analytic geometry by Fermat and Descartes, who showed how points can be represented by pairs or triples of numbers and geometric figures by algebraic equations. This discovery bridged the chasm between geometric and arithmetic concepts that dominated Greek mathematics and prepared for the invention of calculus. The third event was the discovery of non-Euclidean geometry by Gauss, Bolyai, and Lobachevsky (and in a somewhat different context by Riemann). This showed that the axioms of Euclid are not self-evident truths as had been assumed for centuries, and that consistent geometries built on other axioms are possible (see Coxeter's essay in reference 7). The results of this discovery for human thought were stupendous. Only the consequences for mathematics are of interest to us here. The axiomatic method that pervades all modern mathematics is one of these. So, in a certain sense, is mathematical logic and the use of formal languages. So is, finally, the whole proliferation of various geometries in which one begins by assuming only *some* of the familiar properties of the space of everyday experience and then proceeds to develop their logical consequences.

It would seem that by permitting itself this unlimited freedom and by cutting, as it were, the umbilical cord tying geometry to its early experimental origins, this science would lose its connection with reality and would cease to be a tool of science and technology. It is well known that the opposite has taken place.

We will review briefly some subdivisions of modern geometry.

Algebraic Geometry

Today, most high school students get a taste of this discipline when they study conics (ellipses, parabolas, and hyperbolas). These curves, known to the ancient Greeks, are geometric embodiments of simple algebraic equations. An ellipse, for instance, consists of all points in the plane whose coordinates x and y satisfy an equation of the form $(x/a)^2 + (y/b)^2 = 1$, where a and b are two numbers.

Algebraic geometry is concerned with solutions of systems of algebraic equations using a geometric language. A basic aim is to achieve a full understanding of the totality of solutions. In order to obtain this, it is necessary to extend the scope of the algebra and the geometry involved. Modern algebraic geometry studies equations whose coefficients are not only ordinary real or complex numbers, but also elements of more general fields or rings. It considers the geometric configurations defined by such equations not only in the plane or in ordinary three-dimensional space but also in higher-dimensional spaces.

One of the attractions of algebraic geometry is its intimate connection with number theory; intricate algebraic and geometric constructions are sometimes used to obtain number-theoretic results.* Algebraic geometry is now flourishing and attracting some of the most talented young men entering mathematics. We mention two recent developments.

An outstanding problem was whether, given $k-n$ independent algebraic equations in k unknowns, it is possible to represent all solutions of this system by a smooth geometric figure. (More precisely, can one transform the variety defined by this system into a smooth figure by using so-called birational transformations?) The affirmative answer for $n = 1$ was found in the nineteenth century. For $n = 2$ the first purely algebraic proof for systems with coefficients in the complex numbers was given by Zariski about 30 years ago. Ten years later, he solved the case $n = 3$. Recently, the general case (any n) was settled affirmatively by Hironaka.

Another achievement of a quite different nature is the systematic rebuilding of the foundation of algebraic geometry now led by Grothendieck in France. His work, which also leads to solutions of important concrete problems, has influenced many young mathematicians, including those working in other fields.

---

* For instance, "Fermat's last theorem" (a statement made in the seventeenth century and thus far proved only in certain special cases) can be interpreted as follows: let n be an integer greater than 2 and consider the algebraic surface $x^n + y^n = z^n$ in the x,y,z space; are there points on this surface with integral coordinates other than the three points $(0, 0, 0)$, $(1, 0, 1)$, $(0, 1, 1)$? Fermat claimed there are not.

Differential Geometry

Just as the analytic geometry of Fermat and Descartes and its subsequent development into algebraic geometry may be described as applications of algebra to geometry, so differential geometry may be described as the application of calculus to geometry. It reached maturity only when mathematicians learned to live in spaces of more than three dimensions. At this level of abstraction one cannot draw figures but must work with formulas, and the formulas themselves become so complicated that the invention of a convenient notation is a major task. This task was accomplished by Italian geometers toward the turn of the nineteenth century. The "tensor analysis" or "Ricci calculus" created by them seemed at that time an example of monastic mathematics at its most esoteric. But when Einstein was searching for a mathematical language to express ideas of general relativity, he was led, after much inner resistance, as he himself stated, to tensor analysis.

The unexpected application of differential geometry in relativity led to a flowering of this discipline that continues today. The original work in differential geometry was primarily "local"; one studied a limited, usually very small, part of the space under consideration. In modern differential geometry one studies "global" properties, that is, properties of the space as a whole, and one is particularly interested in the connection between local and global properties.

Point Set Topology

This branch of geometry is first of all the study of very general geometric figures in ordinary space. Classical geometry, from the Greeks until the nineteenth century, confined its studies to relatively simple figures—straight lines, triangles, circles, ellipses, and the like. Set theory led mathematicians to consider also "wild" figures—curves without tangents, curves that pass through every point in a square (so-called Peano curves), and so forth. When this kind of mathematics was born, some mathematicians, including even as great a man as Poincaré, dismissed it as a study of freaks. It appeared, however, that the freaks that Poincaré thought were invented by people looking for ugliness appear by themselves in connection with beautiful classical objects (this was observed in the theory of so-called Kleinian groups initiated by Poincaré himself!) and that further investigations reveal beauty and harmony in what first appeared to be a world of chaos.

Another aspect of point set topology is the logical analysis of our most basic ideas about space.

Point set topology played a special role in the development of mathematics in this country, since the unique pedagogical work of R. L. Moore (University of Texas), which is responsible directly or indirectly for so much research activity in mathematics, has been centered about point set topology. (For further information about point set topology, we refer to the essay by Bing in reference 7.)

Algebraic Topology

Topology is concerned with the study of shapes of geometric figures and with qualitative properties of continuous transformations between such figures. The original names of the discipline were analysis situs and later combinatorial topology. In studying qualitative aspects of geometry, one considered first figures composed of the simplest conceivable building blocks—points, straight segments, triangles, tetrahedra, for example. Brouwer, one of the founders of topology, named these building blocks "simplexes." Certain basic figures studied in algebraic topology are called "complexes." They are composed of simplexes in such a way that two simplexes that touch each other have a whole face in common. In studying complexes one pays no attention to their size or shape but only to the way the various simplexes are combined. Hence the name "combinatorial topology." It was changed to "algebraic topology" when it became apparent that the progress of the discipline depended essentially on the use of sophisticated algebraic tools. Today there is available a variety of algebraic aids for the study of topology. In fact, some parts of topology have been completely reduced to algebra, and although the resulting algebraic problems have not been solved completely, they are theoretically solvable in the sense that their effective computability has been established.

We shall describe one basic problem, on the boundary between point set topology and algebraic topology. Does the method of representing a geometric figure as a complex really capture all the geometric properties we want to capture? More precisely, suppose we are given two complexes that are topologically equivalent, that is, such that one can establish a one-to-one correspondence between their points in which nearby points in one complex correspond to nearby points in the other. Can one then subdivide the complexes into finer ones in such a way that the resulting subdivided complexes are "combinatorially equivalent," so that, under an appropriate one-to-one correspondence, vertices of a simplex in one correspond to vertices of a simplex in the other?

The answer may depend on the dimension in which one operates. It is affirmative for dimensions 1, 2, and 3, but Milnor proved about five years ago that it is, in general, negative. On the other hand, the answer is probably affirmative for complexes that have a certain smoothness property, in the technical language for manifolds. (The affirmative answer for the case of three-dimensional manifolds was found by Moise in 1952. His proof was ingenious but elementary. The affirmative answer for certain manifolds of dimension at least 5 has been obtained very recently by the 26-year-old mathematician Sullivan. He draws on many parts of the machinery developed by topologists during the past 20 years. The case of four dimensions appears today to be completely inaccessible.)

One of the most important applications of topology is to analysis, in particular to solving differential equations. One link between topology and analysis is established by the celebrated "Morse theory" of critical points. The recent extension of this theory to infinite dimensional spaces (by Smale and others) promises to be of significance for solving nonlinear partial differential equations.

Differential Topology

In algebraic topology one considers complexes, that is, geometric figures that can be decomposed into simple building blocks, simplexes. Another approach is to consider figures that can be described, near every point, by a system of coordinates, like the ones used in analytic geometry. An example is the surface of a sphere on which points are located by means of the geographic coordinates, latitude and longitude. It is in general impossible to use one system of coordinates for the whole figure. In the case of geographic coordinates on the sphere, for instance, there are "singularities" at the two poles. It is required, however, that we should be able to cover the whole figure by patches in which coordinates can be defined; and it is required that the formulas describing the transition from one coordinate system to another should involve only smooth (differentiable) functions. If a geometric figure can be covered by such coordinate patches, it is called a smooth manifold; if a system of coordinate patches has been defined, we say that we have defined on our figure a differentiable structure.

It had been believed for a long time that whether one does topology of well-behaved figures by complexes or by differentiable manifolds is a matter of technical convenience. It was believed, for instance, that there is essentially only one way in which a differentiable structure can be defined on a reasonable figure. The advantage of the approach through complexes lay in the possibility of using algebra. The advantages of the approach through manifolds lay in the possibility of using analysis, differentiation, and integration. The celebrated theorems of de Rham, which showed that certain numbers characterizing the shape of a figure from the point of view of algebraic topology could also be arrived at by integral calculus, were an early triumph of this approach.

But differential topology as a fully independent discipline was born only in 1952, with Milnor's remarkable discovery that even on a figure as simple from the topological point of view as the seven-dimensional sphere, there is more than one way of defining a differentiable structure. This discovery shared the fate of other fundamental "counterexamples." At first it seemed that the so-called "Milnor spheres" were freaks that their discoverer was ingenious enough to construct, but which could not possibly occur in a reasonable mathematical context. Recently, however, it was discovered that Milnor spheres appear inevitably in the theory of functions of several complex variables. Also, far from being ugly and chaotic, the existence of different differentiable structures reveals a world of hidden harmony and symmetry.

Differential topology has now become one of the most active mathematical disciplines. It is, more than any other branch of topology, connected with differential geometry, the theory of differential equations, and algebraic geometry. In some sense the appearance of differential topology represents the return of topology to its origins in problems of mechanics and differential equations. Here again the unifying tendencies of contemporary mathematics are clearly visible. (An account of the evolution of differential topology will be found in the essay by Gleason in reference 7.)

Lie Groups

We mentioned earlier that a group is an algebraic entity describing symmetry. In the theory of Lie groups (so named after the nine teenth-century Norwegian mathematician, Sophus Lie) geometry, analysis, and algebra are inseparably joined. Lie groups are groups in the ordinary sense that have the added feature of being parameterized, at least locally, by real numbers. (An example is the totality of all displacements of a rigid body. This is a group, since a succession of displacements is again a displacement and every displacement can be canceled by another. A displacement of a rigid body can be described by six numbers, three to tell how some fixed point in the body has been translated and three to tell how the body has been rotated about this point. Thus the group of rigid motions in ordinary space is a six-parameter Lie group.) This parameterization has immediate and far-reaching consequences, because techniques from analysis become applicable and Lie's original concept, the infinitesimal group (now called Lie algebra), assumes a central place in the theory. Geometric objects led naturally to a rich supply of examples, and much effort was made to classify all Lie groups in terms of these examples.

Lie groups play a dominating and unifying role in modern mathematics; they have stimulated significant research in algebra and topology, and such widely different fields as finite-group theory and differential geometry are today strongly influenced by Lie group theory. The "representation theory" of Lie groups, which on occasions has been the source of inspiration of important discoveries in physics, has also suggested entirely new directions in analysis, thereby incorporating and revitalizing large parts of classical analysis.

5

Applied Mathematical Sciences

Fields of mathematical science outside the core are of various kinds. Both computer science and statistics have dual sources of identity and intellectual force, only one of which is mathematical; hence they are more accurately described as partly mathematical sciences. These two already apply to almost as wide a variety of activities as does mathematics itself.

Computer science is both a mathematical science and something else. In its present form it could not exist without mathematics. But it would be utterly unproductive without a piece of machinery—the computer, both as we have access to it at the moment and as we can envisage it in the future.

Modern statistics could not operate without mathematics, especially without the theory of probability. Equally, it could not exist without the challenge of inference in the face of uncertainty and the stimulus of the quantitative aspects of the scientific method. Like computer science, statistics is both a mathematical science and something else.

At the other extreme are fields—mathematical economics, mathematical psychology, mathematical linguistics, among others—that deal with the mathematical aspects of rather specific areas.

At an intermediate level of breadth and identity stand fields that have derived their nature from some area of application, usually a quite broad one. These fields have initially chosen their tools to meet the application area's problems but have grown and developed far enough to have a mathematical character of their own, thereby gaining a certain independence of existence and breadth of application they could not otherwise have had. The outstanding example is physical mathematics, or classical applied mathematics, which has grown out of the mathematics of classical physics to a point where it deals with a wide variety of applications of mathematical analysis. A similarly intermediate field is today growing rapidly in an area stimulated by applications to pure and applied economics and to management and the conduct of operations of all kinds—business, governmental, and military. As yet there is little agreement about this field's name, but its concentration on problems of optimizing any or all of allocation, control, and decision is so evident that we can label it accordingly.

FLUID DYNAMICS: AN EXAMPLE OF PHYSICAL MATHEMATICS

To illustrate the nature of physical mathematics (classical applied mathematics), we shall describe in some detail one of its typical and central subdivisions—the mathematical theory of fluid motion. The description will be followed by a few general comments on related areas.

Both liquids and gases (neutral or ionized) are fluids. The study of fluid motion is, strictly speaking, a part of physics. It has been left, however, for many decades now, largely in the care of applied mathematicians, engineers, astrophysicists, and geophysicists (including meteorologists and oceanographers). Applied mathematics has found in the study of fluid motion some of its most spectacular triumphs and also has suffered some of its, hopefully temporary, notable defeats.

Attempts to describe the motion of fluids mathematically are almost as old as mathematical analysis. The early history of fluid dynamics is associated with names such as Bernoulli, Euler, and D'Alembert. Classical fluid dynamics led to some of the most important developments in mathematics and to techniques and ideas that have found many other applications. Riemann contributed to the basic theory of propagation of strong compression waves. His ideas led to the development of the notion of "characteristics," which greatly influenced the theory of partial differential equations. Much of Hadamard's work was concerned with wave propagation. All this work laid the basis for many of the recent developments in the theory of supersonic flow and shock waves, which occur on the earth (sonic boom associated with supersonic aircraft) as well as in the stars (novas and supernovas).

Much of the classical fluid dynamics of incompressible flow seemed originally to be completely useless as a model for physical reality. For instance, D'Alembert proved that a body moving through fluid experiences no drag. Of course, D'Alembert's derivation neglected viscosity (the tendency of one part of a fluid to pull adjacent parts along with it); but his result was contrary to experience even in cases where viscosity effects seemed to be very insignificant.

Fluid-flow theories applicable to physical reality appeared only in the nineteenth and early twentieth centuries, largely as a response to the needs of aeronautics. A major achievement was Prandtl's theory of the boundary layer, which showed in which cases one can use classical fluid dynamics to obtain physically valid results, and how in such cases the viscosity effects are limited to a small layer of fluid next to a moving body (whence the name "boundary layer"). Boundary-layer theory led, by the way, to important developments in the general theory of differential equations.

Compressibility of air was neglected in aerodynamics that proved sufficient for the engineering needs of the period up to World War II. Interest in high-speed flight required that compressibility be taken into account and that the essentially nonlinear theory of gas flow be faced. While certain mathematical points in that theory are still unexplained, today sufficient theoretical understanding is available for practical needs. The "sound barrier" turned out to be largely imaginary, but the high altitudes achieved in rocket flight necessitated the creation of a new type of fluid dynamics, the dynamics of rarefied gases. This theory contributed to the successful solution of the re-entry problem for earth satellites.

A young and very active discipline of modern fluid dynamics is magnetohydrodynamics, which describes the interaction between electromagnetic fields and conducting liquids or ionized gases (plasmas). We can hope that this subject will contribute as much to the future course of mathematics as did the individual subjects of electromagnetic theory, fluid dynamics, and statistical mechanics. Magnetohydrodynamics has applications to astrophysics (stellar atmospheres and interstellar matter), to the search for a controlled thermonuclear reaction, and to a promising use of ionized-gas "armatures" in generating electric power. The striking spiral structure of many galaxies (including our own) can now be understood in terms of magnetohydrodynamics and statistical dynamics of stellar systems. Here the very old subject of self-gravitating fluids, studied by MacLaurin, Jacobi, Riemann, and Dedekind in another connection, plays a predominant role.

The behavior of stellar systems and rarefied plasmas has been known to be governed by a type of "collisionless Boltzmann equation" and to exhibit "collective behavior." On a still larger scale, the distribution of matter in the universe is often treated in terms of fluids governed by Einstein's general theory of relativity. The question of the existence of gravitational radiation offers challenging nonlinear partial differential equations begging for solution.

In recent years, there has been a great upsurge of the study of fluid mechanics for the purpose of describing phenomena in geophysics (meteorology and oceanography), where the rotation of the earth often plays an essential role. Much of the work was done by applied mathematicians; Von Neumann was among the pioneers in the use of numerical methods for weather prediction (see An Example from the Environmental Sciences: Numerical Weather Prediction, page 108). Problems of hydrodynamic stability, on which work is still flourishing, occur in a variety of ways.

Yet some problems in fluid dynamics, which are almost as old as the science itself, still resist all efforts at mathematical treatment. An outstanding example is turbulence, a phenomenon easily observed by anybody watching the disintegration of the smoke jet from a factory chimney or from a cigarette. Although some of the best minds in physics and mathematics have applied themselves to this problem and have achieved some partial successes, there is at the present little hope for a satisfactory solution in the near future. It is now clear that the existing studies and the still unresolved problems both relate to the broader area of nonlinear random processes.

At the same time, the theory of the fundamental partial differential equations governing the motion of incompressible viscous flow has not been fully developed. It remains a challenging and interesting problem to pure mathematicians and a source of much current stimulation for work.

As mentioned above, there is a similarity between the behavior of stellar systems and that of rarefied plasmas in exhibiting collective behavior. The similarity is not only in the basic ideas but also, surprisingly, in the details. Concepts used in fluid mechanics are also useful when continuum mechanics deals with other material—elastic solids, plastic solids, and bodies exhibiting both flow and elastic properties. The study of the basic laws of continuum mechanics depends heavily on the concepts of "covariance" (i.e., the assertion that physical laws would remain in the same form no matter what observer is making the description).

Indeed, the concepts and methods that originate in one branch of applied mathematics are often applicable to other branches. Once the theory is put into mathematical form, even in a form not yet deserving serious interest of core mathematics, it could be of basic importance to other branches of applied mathematics. Equilibrium, stability and instability, wave motion, linear versus nonlinear processes, reversible versus irreversible processes, entropy—and one can name many more—are certainly concepts whose applications are general. The mathematical theory of economics makes use of several of them. The new science of information theory, with its fascinating coding theorems and important applications to practical problems in communication engineering, also uses the concept of entropy.

These observations demonstrate that much of classical applied mathematics has a tendency to merge into a coherent whole across traditional scientific disciplines, adding to the strength and usefulness of the entire area of activity.

STATISTICS

Statisticians easily recognize other statisticians as such, though they are often surprised by the fields in which they work and the tools that they use. It is now almost three quarters of a century since Karl Pearson turned from graphical mechanics to the application of algebra and differential equations to problems arising in the analysis of experimental and observational data. The mathematical theory of probability, now considered part of core mathematics, has applications to the "adjustment of data," first in surveying and astronomy and then in many other fields, going back to the work of Gauss and Laplace a century earlier.

A variety of traditions have merged in contemporary statistics, not only the application of the theory of probability and the more quantitative aspects of scientific method but the numerical skills of the economist and the meteorologist and the data-handling skills that have been served by one form or another of automation since the invention by Hollerith of the punched-card machine in the last century. Today, statisticians are concerned with how it would seem we might well make inferences, how we do make inferences, and how we might and do collect, process, and digest data in a wide variety of fields.

Karl Pearson's willingness to attack the dimensions of crabs, the inheritance of intelligence, and the mechanisms of evolution with mathematical techniques, however, signaled the opening of a new era, one in which new problems and mathematical theories have shared responsibility for intellectual stimulation, and where, in one field after another, the statistician has done much to introduce workers in that field to new ideas and new ways of thinking as well as to new techniques. The basic ideas of quantitative scientific method, of uncertainty, and of elementary mathematical models have been brought into many fields by statisticians. Agriculture, biology, and medicine; insurance and actuarial techniques; industrial production and market research; psychology, sociology, and anthropology; all have benefited.

Once statistics was thought of as confined to the study and manipulation of large masses of data. Such problems are still among the most challenging, but the problems of doing a good job of converting three or five or ten numbers into suitably qualified conclusions are today at least equally important. Individuals, corporate bodies, governments, scientists, engineers, economists—all use a wide variety of statistical techniques to assess "what the data say" and thus to guide them in their deliberations and actions. Wherever the evidence is less than complete or bears only indirectly on the point at issue—in truth, almost everywhere—there is a place for statistics in untangling the data and assessing the conclusion.

Karl Pearson, "Student" (W. S. Gossett), and R. A. Fisher took leading parts in the early development of a mathematical statistics of wide application. During the years between the two world wars, new statistical methods and new methods for arranging experiments made major contributions to the development of agricultural technology. (One of the three leaders of the first American seminar on R. A. Fisher's analysis of variance was later president of the Pioneer Hybrid Corn Breeding Company.) Statistical techniques made our agricultural progress possible, while the needs of agricultural experimentation called whole areas of statistics into existence.

Beginning in the early 1920's, farsighted men at Bell Telephone

Laboratories recognized the importance of statistics' potential in industrial production. Walter Shewhart founded and developed the theory of statistical quality control, and Harold Dodge led in the development of sampling schemes for inspecting mass-produced items. Both of these techniques are sometimes given major credit for significant contributions to the success of the Allied production effort in World War II. In particular, statistical quality control was a major factor in the early success of the plutonium-production process at Hanford. After the war, the application of statistical techniques to the experimental improvement of industrial production processes made outstanding progress, particularly in connection with chemical processes.

Stimulated by Student and Shewhart, J. Neyman and E. S. Pearson developed the first of the modern mathematical theories of formally optimized inference in the latter 1930's. During the same years and in the decade that followed, the mathematical theory of sampling developed to meet the needs of studying large groups of people, farms, business firms, and many other things by observing relatively small samples. The sample survey thus became effective, efficient, and irreplaceable.

Wartime needs for even more efficient inspection led Abraham Wald, once a pure mathematician, in one sleepless night, to the basic theory of sequential analysis and seeded his later work on statistical decision theory (to which a brief introduction is given in the essay by Kiefer in reference 7). The needs of a variety of problems in geophysics (waves on the ocean, earthquakes, gusts that disturb airplanes) and in engineering (e.g., tracking radars) demanded new tools to isolate phenomena tagged by their frequencies of oscillation. Statistical spectrum analysis developed rapidly, spreading into a wide range of applications, including recent congressional inquiries into the proper adjustment of economic series, such as unemployment, for the season of the year.

The implications of psychological and educational testing have often been discussed and will be discussed many times again, demonstrating the ever-increasing importance of these techniques in our lives. The selection of test material and the study of individual and interrelated behavior of tests has had to be carried out in a statistical way, demanding and receiving the development of new statistical techniques.

Qualitative studies of a national economy and of the economic environment of single firms share the difficulties of (1) complexities requiring explicit treatment of many variables and (2) limitation of available data almost to the point where there are not enough to obtain meaningful answers. As a result, econometricians have developed, and have stimulated others to develop, another broad area of statistical technique—econometrics. For instance, important issues in the recent Federal Communications Commission hearing about telephone rates came down to questions of statistical technique and statistical appropriateness.

Most areas of biological and medical research have come to depend on statistical techniques. Experimenters routinely use methods that grew up in agricultural research, supplemented by special statistical techniques appropriate to the effectiveness of drugs and poisons. The study of epidemic and occupational disease calls on other techniques and poses very difficult problems.

The study of medical and surgical performance is an even more difficult field. The recent national study of one of the anesthetics most used for surgery fortunately showed certain specific suspicions to be unfounded. Yet it turned up suggestive differences between postoperative death rates that may prove to be associated with the anesthetics used. These apparent differences could not have been seen without the use of statistical techniques not in existence when the study began; the untangling of their true nature and causes will require both better statistical techniques and better data, each of which stimulates the other.

The arrival of modern electronic computation opened many new opportunities in almost every field of statistics. Routine seasonal adjustment of economic time series no longer calls for an expert; a dollar's worth of computer time does it. The periods of the natural vibrations of the earth would never have been measured without computer processing, and we would have known much less about the earth's interior. Yet most of the large-scale challenges involved in harnessing modern computing systems to the effective analysis of data have hardly been tackled.

Just as it is still a methodological science, a computational science, and a behavioral science, statistics continues to be a mathematical science. Its health depends on effective exchanges of results and problems with workers in a wide variety of fields. The increasing variety of applications has increased the needs for the invention of new techniques appropriate to new problems. Throughout the areas of statistical technique that have been developed over the last four or five decades there are great needs for modernization.

There is a need to develop probabilistic models for new phenomena, to study the properties of these models, and to investigate statistical procedures appropriate for them. Most formal optimization of statistical methods has been carried out for classes of distributions that are too narrow (normal or Gaussian) or too broad (all continuous distributions) to correspond satisfactorily to practice. The impact of the computer not only on what is possible but also on what is reasonable in statistical techniques has been only barely thought about and only in very special cases. Communicating results to people can be much more effective once we understand how to use computer-produced graphs and pictures. Adequate treatment for the nonexperimental observations of behavioral science and medicine requires rethinking of the ideas whose formalizations underlie statistical techniques. These are but four of many directions in which progress is being demanded.

Computer Science

Automatic high-speed computing is scarcely 20 years old. Nevertheless, it already constitutes one of the nation's most valuable scientific and economic resources.

Until automatic electronic digital computers first became commercially available around 1950, most persons took at least 10 seconds to multiply two moderately large numbers. With today's electronic computers, the same multiplication can be done nearly 10,000,000 times faster. In comparison, the speedup in travel between walking and going by jet is by a factor of approximately 100, while that in communication between sound and radio waves is by a factor of approximately 1,000,000. These changes in rates of transportation and communication have completely remade the world. The even greater speedups in information processing are remaking our world again. It will be many years before our capacity to exploit the new computers fully will catch up with even their present capabilities. Meanwhile, rapid advances in speed and in the capacity of computers to store information continue.

The development of computing is accelerating the penetration of mathematics into old and new fields of human endeavor. In fact, the original purpose for developing computers was the numerical solution of mathematical problems. The success achieved in this direction has been phenomenal. Calculations that required years of effort by teams of people can now be done in a matter of minutes. Mathematical problems that were thought inaccessible to effective numerical treatment are now solved as a matter of routine. During any rocket launch, for instance, dozens of nonlinear ordinary differential equations are being solved in a completely automatic manner.

Numerical analysis, the branch of mathematics concerned with the invention and evaluation of methods for mathematical calculation, has been revitalized by the advent of the computer but has so far been unable to keep pace with technological developments. (See Davis' essay in reference 7.) Computers vastly increased the importance of parts of numerical analysis and made others completely obsolete. Carrying out a stupendous number of arithmetic operations in solving a single problem introduced a host of difficulties associated with the limited precision and range of computer numbers. (See the essay by Forsythe in reference 7.) Meeting these difficulties has led to an array of new and powerful algorithms for solving mathematical problems.

It is important to realize the variety of fields in which computing has become an important tool. One of these is mathematics, but this is a relatively minor fraction of the total volume of computing done today. Others include experimental and theoretical physics, business-data processing, economic planning, library work, engineering design (from transportation systems to computers themselves), education, inventory management, police operations, space science, musical performance, and content analyses of documents. One can speak without reservations of a computerization of our culture that is already broader, though less deep, than its mathematization.

The modern computer can do many things. The logical possibility of building a universal computing machine that in principle can do anything any computing machine can do was first recognized, as a theorem in mathematical logic, by A. M. Turing. This discovery influenced the work of the mathematician Von Neumann, who contributed the crucially important suggestion that computers should store their instructions together with their data.

The practical importance of computing to our society can be judged from the direct annual cost to the federal government of acquiring and operating electronic computers in 1967. It was in the range of $2 billion. (Source: *The New York Times,* 25 January 1966, p. 21, quoting the President's budget message.)

The near-universality of a modern computer means that it can perform almost any manipulation of symbols. The breathtaking future perspectives to which this may someday lead are described in an essay by J. T. Schwartz on prospects of computer science.[7]

In particular, computers can be used for direct simulation of complicated technological, natural, and social phenomena, where computer instructions play the role of formulas in setting up a formal model. Such models are as truly mathematical as those expressed in formulas. Lists of computer instructions can be long and interrelated in complicated ways and still be executable. If many details must be treated, examples of behavior can be obtained by direct simulation when general results cannot be obtained from similarly complicated lists of mathematical formulas. Examples of problems that have been treated by direct simulation include highway traffic control, the design of telephone networks, and the design of concrete shields for nuclear reactors.

Just as zoology is the study of animals and animal behavior, so computer science is the study of computers and computation. Three aspects are currently of outstanding importance:

1. The design and analysis of computer hardware—the components and total electronic and mechanical systems that comprise computers;

2. The design and analysis of computer software—the basic languages and resident programs essential to convert bare hardware into productive computing systems, including control programs, compilers, and time-sharing executives;

3. The methodology of solving problems with computers—those techniques that are common to solving broad classes of problems, as opposed to the preparation of individual programs to solve single problems. One of these techniques is the appropriate representation of complex information.

Today, computer science is, among other things, a mathematical science. As Professor Allen Newell describes it in his memorandum to COSRIMS:

Computer science shares with mathematics a concern with formalism and a concern with the manipulation of symbols. It also shares with mathematics the role of handmaiden to all of science and technology. It shares with electrical engineering the concern with the design and construction of information processing systems that accomplish ends.

It shares with all of engineering a concern with the process of design, considered as an intellectual endeavor. It shares with linguistics a concern with language and communication. It shares with psychology a special concern with forms of information processing that result in intelligent behavior, broadly viewed. It shares with the library sciences a concern with how to store and retrieve large amounts of information, either as documents or as facts. It has both theoretical aspects, as in the study of automata, and experimental ones, as in the discovery of new types of systems through programming them and exploring their behavior. All of these shared problems with other parts of science and technology imply that the future status of computer science is still indeterminate. It may permanently become one of the mathematical sciences. It may become an autonomous science, such as geology. The result is genuinely in doubt, because "science" is a social construct, shaped as much by social forces as by anything intrinsic to its subject matter.

Lying as it does across the research fields of mathematics, electronic engineering, linguistics, psychology, among others, computer science, though still somewhat formless and unfocused, is also an independent entity. Both government and universities tend to view it as such, as is evidenced by dozens of university computer science departments and a separate Office for Computing Activities within the National Science Foundation. As a mathematical science, computer science emphasizes the constructive, problem-solving, algorithmic aspect of mathematics, in contrast with the structure aspects, often emphasized in core mathematics. As a young field that must respond to soaring demands for knowledge at all levels of specialization, computer science can use the cooperation of mathematicians in creating a solid body of knowledge.

Computer science is at once abstract and pragmatic. The focus on actual computing systems introduces the pragmatic component; the central questions are economic ones like the relations among speed, accuracy, and cost of a proposed computation, and the hardware and software organization required. The often better understood theoretical questions of existence and computability provide an important conceptual basis for the study of the more pressing questions. (And these in turn have led to new mathematical research in such questions as degrees of finite computability.) On the other hand, computer science deals with information—in an abstract way. The meanings of symbols and numbers may change from application to application, just as they do in every application of mathematics. Thus computer science shares the main goal of mathematics—to create a basic structure in terms of inherently defined concepts that is not bound to any particular application. Computer scientists have barely begun the creation of such a basic structure and are still mainly concerned with exploring what computers can and cannot do economically.

So far the most mathematical components of computer science are numerical analysis and the theory of programming languages.

The first computers were programmed in *machine language,* a language that might be likened to microsyllables of human speech. Typical of machine language is an instruction saying in effect: "Add the number in cell 4565 to the number in arithmetic register A, and leave the answer in register A." The solution of substantial mathematical problems in terms of such instructions expended many man-months of tedious, repetitive human labor. After some years, it was realized that computers, with their infinite capacity for carrying out details, could themselves be instructed to translate an *algebraic language* into machine language. Thus human beings could write programs in higher-level languages like Fortran and Algol and save perhaps 99 percent of their programming time. Soon such algebraic languages and the complex translation programs (called *compilers*) required to translate them automatically became objects of study in themselves. It was learned that programming languages that were easily described in the terms of mathematical linguistics were both more effective and easier to write compilers for. Thus computer science profited from research in mathematical linguistics whose motivation had been entirely different. By now the number of algebraic languages has grown out of hand, and research is actively going on in automating the writing of compilers by other programs, called *compiler-compilers.*

By its speed of processing information and making decisions, the electronic digital computer can be an extension of the human mind with capacities in this direction incomparably greater than those of any mental aid heretofore available. A great deal of contemporary research in computer science goes into designing hardware, languages, and software for the effective coupling of human minds to computers. The goal is to match the highly versatile and imaginative human mind, which is slow, with the extremely fast, accurate, and tireless computer, which lacks initiative. It appears that one acceptable solution will take the form of *time-sharing.* In this, a computer rotates its "attention" among some dozens of human beings, each at his own console, just as a master chess player can play simultaneous chess with a roomful of less-skilled opponents. Creating effective and economic time-shared *computer utility* will require the combined skills of mathematicians, operations analysts, computer scientists, and engineers, since extremely complex problems are involved. This is a field of very active research in computer science today.

In addition to the reasonably successful methods developed for numerical computation and programming languages, algebraic (nonnumerical) methods for some classes of problems are now emerging. Methods for handling pictorial data have been formalized for large classes of pictures. There still remains an almost unlimited array of topics that are not being treated systematically. This is the frontier of computer science. It includes a large number of nonnumerical problems, as well as such problems as executive control (scheduling, allocation, handling, interruptions) and simulation of intelligent behavior.

Optimized Allocation, Control, and Decisions

The needs of economic theory for results about allocation, those of management practice for approaches to decisions (which can usually be cast in terms of allocation), and those of engineering operation for patterns of control (whether in trajectory choice or the feedback control of production machinery) all lead to a single interrelated complex of problems, concepts, and results. In almost every case, these problems can be described in terms of maximizing or minimizing—i.e., optimizing—some criterion subject to constraints on the variables.

Separately developed traditions are now being merged into a coherent body of concepts and results. Workers in the field have come to recognize its unity as more important than its diversity. The needs of economists, managers, and engineers for explicit guidance in choosing answers, and for as many explicit answers as possible, have anchored this area close to the frontier. There is interest in a procedure that in principle describes a solution, but ordinarily only as a step toward a feasible procedure for finding actual solutions. Since feasibility is a matter of computation, exactly what computing tools are available is vitally important. This whole area is therefore intimately bound up with computer systems and with machine arithmetic.

An interesting mathematical development in this area was Von Neumann's and Morgenstern's "theory of games and economic behavior," which tackled the strategic and mathematical problems of simultaneous optimization of rewards by two or more game players or economic competitors.

A major thread began with linear programming, the problem of optimizing a linear function of many variables when subject to very many simple linear inequalities. Linear programming problems were first systematically attacked in the 1930's, in Russia by Kantorovich, whose results escaped notice for many years, and in the United States at about the same time by Koopmans and Hitchcock. The field's growth in the United States was greatly stimulated in 1947 by Dantzig's discovery of a method that made possible the solution of reasonably complex problems with then available computer facilities. A burst of industrial applications soon stretched both the practical and the theoretical boundaries of the subject. Nonlinear programming was introduced, in which the function to be maximized was generalized from a linear function of the given variables, and the constraining inequalities were also generalized. The fact that many practical problems involve units that cannot be subdivided (how many dresses can be cut from a bolt of cloth?) now demanded, and received, an effective theory of integer programming.

A third line of development involved problems of simultaneous allocations: How can n persons be best assigned to n jobs? How can many factories best ship their products to many customers? Some allocation problems have proved to be intrinsically very difficult: What pattern of warehouse locations will minimize shipping costs? What is the shortest route passing through every one of a list of cities? Treated directly, such problems have a characteristic irreducible complexity, since the entire solution must be examined simultaneously.

Certain types of these problems have fortunately been found to be reducible to problems of linear and nonlinear programming and have thus become much more easily soluble. Others have yielded to special algorithms, and the remainder pose serious problems for the techniques of combinatorial analysis and the capacities of modern computing systems.

A fourth line of development involved dynamic programming or the theory of multistage decision processes, which treats problems in which a number of decisions are made over a period of time. The maintenance of inventories in the face of uncertain demand, where there must be repeated decisions of whether and how much to order, poses a typical problem, as do the scheduling of production, equipment replacement, the conversion of stored water to power, and a wide variety of queuing processes.

As these lines of development continued, perspectives broadened, and the field matured, linear and nonlinear programming and dynamic programming fused together into mathematical programming.

A fifth line of development, carried on vigorously both in the Soviet Union and in the United States, involved the optimum control of systems reasonably thought of as tracing a path. When choosing a rocket trajectory that will require least use of fuel, the path is physical. When deciding how the temperatures in a chemical reaction vessel should change to maximize production of the desired chemical, the path is symbolic. The general mathematical problem is the same, and the same mathematical results are applicable. In many ways, these problems of control theory are continuous-time analogs of the problems of dynamic programming. Both lines of development have contributed ideas to one another, with control theory more frequently taking the lead, since continuous time—with a decision every instant—requires much more sophisticated mathematical techniques and much deeper mathematical results.

Allocation is the immediate end of the theory of games and a consequence of most applications of mathematical programming. Control is the aim of control theory and many applications of dynamic programming. Decisions have to be made in every case. Optimization of some prescribed function is the common thread that links all these lines of development together. Opinions differ on whether the area thus described has already become a clearly identifiable field of mathematical science. If not yet, it soon will become one.

OTHER AREAS

The fields of mathematical science outside the core will continue to make increasing contributions. They will require deepening mathematical education and broadening mathematical literacy among their own workers. This places a great responsibility on university and college faculty in the mathematical sciences. They must provide instruction in core mathematics, including its own latest and most useful concepts, approaches, and results, which alone will strain their capacities. In addition, they must provide instruction that identifies and illustrates the multifaceted role of mathematics in our society.

6

Examples of Mathematics in Use

Many years ago Auguste Comte claimed that a science is a science only insofar as it is mathematical. The mathematization of physical science has been going on for centuries, that of the life and behavioral sciences for a shorter time. Engineering, which is a technology based on physical science, has always used mathematics as an essential tool. The mathematization of a wide variety of other technologies is in process. Accordingly, an exhaustive review of the penetration of mathematics into various areas of human endeavor would require volumes. In this chapter we describe a few typical examples: physics—a science completely mathematized almost from its very inception; engineering design—a fully mathematized technology; mathematics in the newer environmental sciences—specifically, numerical weather prediction; economics—in which the penetration of mathematics is about a hundred years old; the technology of management and operations—in which mathematization is a World War II development.

Clearly we have omitted many important examples. See, for some specific instances, the essays by Cohen on mathematics in biology, by Lederberg on some uses of mathematics in chemistry, and by Harris on mathematical linguistics.[7]

The degree of mathematization, the sophistication of mathematical tools used, and the lasting intellectual value so far achieved by the use of mathematics vary widely from field to field, as we shall comment at the close of this chapter.

101

Mathematics and Physics

Physics is an experimental science concerned with the material world around us. The aim, as physicists define it today, is to describe and to correlate the multitude of experimental phenomena in terms of theoretical concepts formulated in the language of mathematics. Why natural phenomena should be describable in the language of mathematics is a matter of controversy. (For instance, E. Wigner entitled a lecture "The Unreasonable Effectiveness of Mathematics in the Natural Sciences.") Yet it is indisputable, and indeed usually taken for granted, that natural phenomena have been so described with brilliant success.

Because physics deals with quantitative measurements, mathematics comes into physics naturally as an aid for computation and as a tool for the logical operations in theoretical developments. The traditional main branches of mathematics—algebra, analysis, and geometry—have been extensively used in many fields of research in physics in this way. As soon as computers were developed, physicists immediately began to use them to great advantage, to aid in data processing as well as to solve numerical problems.

While mathematics plays an important role in physics in the manner just described, it plays, at the same time, a far more important role at a more fundamental level. In fact, mathematics supplies many of the basic concepts that physicists use to describe natural phenomena. For example, the abstract mathematical concept of noncommutative multiplication lies at the foundation of quantum mechanics. Non-Euclidean geometry is the very starting point of general relativity. There are physicists who believe that analytic continuation is a mathematical concept needed to describe the physical principle of causality.

As one reviews the development of physics through the centuries, starting from the early studies of astronomy and Newtonian mechanics, proceeding through the nineteenth century formulation of electromagnetic phenomena and of the theory of heat and thermodynamics, and then to the modern development of relativity, quantum mechanics, and high-energy physics, one is struck with the increasingly abstract and sophisticated nature of the mathematical concepts that it was necessary to introduce for the description of natural phenomena. Such observation was undoubtedly behind the remark of the late British physicist, Jeans, that God is a mathematician. Some examples of the sophisticated mathematical concepts that have been introduced into physics in recent years are found in the essays by Dyson and Wightman in reference 7. We quote from an article by the great physicist P. A. M. Dirac [*Proc. Roy. Soc., 133,* 66 (1931)]:

The steady progress of physics requires for its theoretical formulation a mathematics that gets continually more advanced. This is only natural and to be expected. What, however, was not expected by the scientific workers of the last century was the particular form that the line of advancement of the mathematics would take, namely, it was expected that the mathematics would get more and more complicated, but would rest on a permanent basis of axioms and definitions, while actually the modern physical developments have required a mathematics that continually shifts its foundations and gets more abstract. Non-Euclidean geometry and noncommutative algebra, which were at one time considered to be purely fictions of the mind and pastimes for logical thinkers, have been found to be very necessary for the description of general facts of the physical world. It seems likely that this process of increasing abstraction will continue in the future and that advance in physics is to be associated with a continual modification and generalization of the axioms at the base of the mathematics rather than with a logical development of any one mathematical scheme on a fixed foundation.

Many physicists believe that the central problem they face today, namely the structure of atomic nuclei and their constituent parts (also known as high-energy physics), may well be solvable only upon the introduction of mathematical concepts not hitherto used in physics and perhaps as yet unknown to mathematicians. Be this as it may, it has been repeatedly demonstrated that a sense of form and an appreciation of elegance, abstraction, and generalization, which are the hallmarks of good mathematical development, are often also the characteristics of the new breakthroughs in physical insight. In fact, what one refers to as physical ideas often derive from properties of abstract mathematical concepts, which turn out to have widespread and deep-rooted applicability in natural phenomena. In reviewing the interplay between mathematics and one branch of physics, M. J. Lighthill [*J. Roy. Aeronaut. Soc., 64,* 375 (1960)] observed that an important task of mathematics is to generate new physical ideas, that is,

. . . ideas which have been originated by mathematical investigation but which later become amenable to almost exclusively physical description, and whose properties, although first derived mathematically, become familiar and are commonly described in purely physical terms. The value of physical ideas in practical work, of course, is their elasticity. Provided that they are sound ideas, such as those thrown up as the genuinely appropriate physical description of the mathematical solution of some well-defined class of problem, they usually show a splendid capacity to stand up to distortion of the problem, and indeed to radical changes and complication in its conditions, and still give the right guidance about what needs to be done.

It is worth remarking that this in fact holds for practically all applications of mathematics.

The relationship between physics and mathematics is by no means a one-way street. While physics uses mathematical concepts, mathematics draws inspiration and stimulation from the physicists' need for new mathematics. The invention of calculus, of differential geometry, of the ergodic theory, all represent mathematical developments stimulated by physical problems. We quote from a recent report by physicists (reference 11, page 162):

Through centuries of intimate contact, theoretical physics and mathematics have interacted strongly to their mutual benefit. Theoretical physics uses the concepts developed in mathematics to formulate descriptions of natural phenomena. Mathematics, in turn, is stimulated in its direction of development by the problems posed by physics. In recent years, the influence of theoretical physics on the development of mathematics seems to have weakened. However, there are still many conspicuous examples of mathematical development influenced by physics: for example, the theory of unbounded operators, the representation theory of noncompact groups, and the theory of distributions. It would be rash to believe that natural phenomena would not again, in the future, as in the past, serve as the fountainhead for important directions of research in mathematics.

The tendency for core mathematics as a whole to move away from physics may be an inevitable characteristic of the mathematics of this century. [See, e.g., M. Stone, "The Revolution in Mathematics," *American Mathematical Monthly, 68,* 715 (1961).] It would be detrimental to both disciplines if this tendency were allowed to take the extreme form of isolating the mathematicians and physicists from mutual intellectual contacts. To forestall such eventuality it is highly important that at the undergraduate, graduate, and postgraduate levels students be given the chance to be exposed to the exciting basic developments of each of the two disciplines.

MATHEMATICAL SCIENCES IN ENGINEERING

The uses of mathematics in engineering represent one of the best recognized as well as one of the most important manifestations of the general mathematization of our culture. Whether one looks at relatively old fields, like civil and mechanical engineering, or relatively new ones, like nuclear technology or electronics, one finds a steady increase in the amount and sophistication of the mathematics used. Information theory is a well-known example. It involves very deep mathematical problems, but its dramatic development was stimulated by the practical need of communications or electronics engineers for a measure of the job of transmitting a given class of messages through a given medium. Modern developments in aerodynamics depend on the desire to build aircraft and missiles flying at higher and higher speeds. It is found, as expected, that the more advanced the technology, the more sophisticated are the basic concepts involved, and the more they depend on mathematics. It is often impossible to understand the concepts used by engineers (even such basic ones as impedance matching, reduction of drag by interference, and subharmonic resonance) without using mathematics.

One form that increased mathematization often takes is development of more precise theories to take advantage of concurrent advances in other directions. For example, a margin of safety of 4:1 has frequently been used in structural design. Such a factor of safety would be utterly unworkable in the design of most missiles; the missiles would be too heavy to get off the ground. Margins of safety as low as 20 to 30 percent are sometimes used. To live with such factors one must have a much more accurate knowledge of aerodynamic forces, natural modes of vibration in the body, and stress distribution than he would otherwise need. Of course, one must also have very good control of the materials and processes that make up the final structure. However, this merely illustrates the common fact that to take maximum advantage of improved technology, advances on the theoretical side and on the physical side must go hand in hand.

New mathematical techniques, particularly in conjunction with computers, are frequently used also in situations where old-fashioned "hand" methods would be too slow or too laborious. For example, the analysis of mathematical models is extensively used in modern civil engineering—an analysis made possible by the existence of large-scale computing machines. The mathematical formulation often leads to linear programming. Prediction of satellite orbits, guided and controlled, is another activity involving careful mathematical formulation and extensive numerical calculations. Once a computational program is well designed, the work is routine and repetitive, but the original formulation often involves deep insight, which can be acquired only by mathematical analysis. The design of gas turbines is another example of the use of computers.

Fluid mechanics, one of the best-established areas of applied mathematics, is important in several engineering fields. The noise produced by jet aircraft and the shock waves associated with supersonic flight must be understood in detail before remedies and improvements can be suggested and designed; combustion instability leads to critical problems in the development of rockets; and systematic progress in minimizing the devastating effects of tornadoes cannot be expected until the understanding of atmospheric dynamics has greatly improved.

The field of electronics and communications is particularly rich in the applications of mathematics. Some of these are like representative problems in other engineering disciplines. For example, lumped circuit theory, both linear and nonlinear, has many points of resemblance to similar areas in mechanics. For continuous media, many problems in electromagnetic field theory are at least broadly similar to typical problems in fluid mechanics or elasticity. The design of radio antennas, for example, can be based on wave-interference effects similar to those that figure in airplane and ship design. More generally, the study of the propagation of radio signals involves a variety of special problems that have challenged such great mathematical physicists as Sommerfeld and such great mathematicians as Hermann Weyl. In recent years, still more complicated mathematical questions have arisen in the study of plasmas, a field of increasing importance in many areas of electrical engineering.

The most fundamental applications of mathematics to electronics and communications, however, are found at the conceptual level. These normally stem from situations in which mathematics offers the best language in which to express both the original engineering problem and the final result. Such situations arise because electricity itself is an intangible that can hardly be described except through mathematics, and because electrical systems are frequently so extensive and complicated that considerations of mathematical regularity and simplicity must be paramount in laying them out.

Perhaps the most elementary example is furnished by the mathematical concept of an impedance. This, though engineers seldom realize it, is strictly a mathematical artifice, a nonphysical "imaginary" quantity by means of which the real currents and voltages in which the engineer is finally interested can be calculated conveniently. Its use becomes a necessity when we deal, as we frequently must, with circuits containing dozens or hundreds of elements. The use of transform methods, established in communications engineering for many years, provides another example. No communication engineer could possibly deal with the variety of signals he must meet in practice without the help of the concept of a frequency spectrum. In more recent years, concepts from mathematical logic have turned out to be an important basis for switching and computer circuits. The best example, however, is probably furnished by information theory. The identification of communication engineering and mathematical logic as two systems that are both concerned largely with the manipulation of arbitrary symbols according to formal rules, made possible by information theory, tremendously broadened the horizon of the communication engineer and at a stroke opened to him vast areas of mathematics as a source of ideas for particular ciphers and coding schemes.

It may happen that the same engineering objective may best be served first by one physical technique and then by another, generating new mathematical problems as they evolve. An example is furnished by surveying, which goes back to classical times and may be regarded as the generator of both geometry and trigonometry. The basic techniques in this case were, of course, optical. With the invention of other instruments such as the telescope, the sextant, and the chronometer a few centuries ago, and greater interest in accurate navigation, still more complicated problems of the same nature emerged. In modern times the basic technique is electronic, as represented by radio networks like LORAN or by navigation satellites. Here the important questions turn on analysis of the coherence and other statistical characteristics of the signal. Still more complicated problems of statistical signal analysis occur in connection with the "surveying" of the solar system by means of radar signals bounced off the nearer planets.

Almost the converse situation occurs when several branches of engineering may be involved in a single system. Here the fact that they can all be dealt with mathematically may be all that holds the situation together. An example is furnished by missiles, which typically involve not only aerodynamics and structural mechanics, but chemistry through the propulsion system and ablative coating and electronics through the control and guidance equipment. They may all be involved if, for example, the missile is required to execute a violent maneuver, and it is only the fact that they are all relatively well understood mathematically that makes it possible to design the system as a whole.

In general, modern engineering systems are too large, complex, and precisely integrated to be designed by empirical test. They must be thoroughly analyzed mathematically in advance of testing in order to obtain reasonable assurance of success.

These diverse applications include many unifying mathematical threads, which deserve to be identified as areas of applied mathematics worth studying on their own account. Once this basic level has been reached, the knowledge gained applies to other branches of technology. Thus problems of transient loading in mechanical systems benefit from techniques originally developed for communications, and chemical and aeronautical engineers work on problems of blood flow and contribute to the advance of medical science.

An Example from the Environmental Sciences: Numerical Weather Prediction

The environmental sciences include earth sciences, oceanography, atmospheric sciences, telecommunications sciences, and aeronomy. Some of the most difficult and sophisticated mathematical problems in the environmental sciences arise from efforts to study the atmosphere and the oceans by means of mathematical models in the form of deterministic fluid systems. This leads to nonlinear partial differential equations subject to rather general boundary and initial conditions. The most successful attempts to treat these problems have involved the use of high-speed computers.

Of special day-to-day importance are the numerical methods of weather prediction now in regular use. The National Meteorological Center* provides, on an operational round-the-clock basis, guidance material to all the national forecast services, as well as to foreign services, under the auspices of the United Nations. The guidance material consists of large-scale wind and weather patterns over the entire northern hemisphere. The basis for this is the approximate numerical solution on large electronic computers of hydrodynamic and thermodynamic partial differential equations constituting a mathematical model for the behavior of the atmosphere.

---

* Of the Weather Bureau, Environmental Science Services Administration, U.S. Department of Commerce. The Center was established in 1954 in Suitland, Maryland, expressly for numerical weather prediction.

The general idea of mathematical weather prediction dates from the first few years of the twentieth century. Detailed pioneering proposals and experiments in weather prediction through the approximate solution of relevant hydrodynamic and thermodynamic equations go back to the British scientist L. F. Richardson[12] in the early 1920's. Richardson's forecasts were not successful, the most fundamental reason for this being his violation of a then unknown stability criterion for numerical processes in the solution of partial differential equations (discovered in 1928 by Courant, Friedrichs, and Lewy).

Another reason for the failure of Richardson's forecasts was insufficient data. It was not until the 1930's and early 1940's that empirical observations began to approach the frequency and detail needed for successful attempts at weather prediction on a mathematical basis. In particular, the new upper-air observational network developed during the 1930's elucidated the dynamics of the so-called jet stream, a great meandering river of air, five to eight miles high and hundreds of miles wide, which loops completely around the northern hemisphere at middle latitudes. The jet stream, together with important vorticity-conservation ideas in its mathematical modeling, has turned out to be the key to large-scale weather prediction in the northern hemisphere.

A third difficulty that would almost certainly have defeated Richardson's original 1922 proposals for numerical weather prediction was the lack of facilities for high-speed computation on the intricate and massive scale needed. He had visualized a giant "weather factory" staffed by an estimated 64,000 human computers busily engaged in obtaining approximate solutions for the appropriate partial differential equations of hydrodynamics and thermodynamics. Looking back, experts today feel it would hardly have been possible to organize such an operation to produce timely weather forecasts. This is, however, the kind of task for which the modern high-speed electronic computer is ideally adapted. The first such computers appeared in the late 1940's. John Von Neumann played a vital role both in the logical design of these computers and in their first successful use in weather calculations in 1948.

During the succeeding years, computers have become steadily more powerful, in speed, versatility, and capacity. Thus, weather calculations that required 24 hours in 1948 were being performed in five minutes by 1951. These and subsequent advances in computer design have been paralleled by advances in research on numerical weather prediction. The relatively simple equations defining the first models for the atmosphere have been extensively refined and elaborated. The early models carried no detail of the vertical structure of the atmosphere, but rather only a vertical average of its motion. By mid-1962, however, a system allowing for three vertical levels had become the principal operational model at the National Meteorological Center. This in turn was replaced, in mid-1966, by a six-level model.

In addition, over the past 20 years considerable advances have been achieved in the methods of numerical analysis used in weather prediction. Many aspects of the numerical techniques are still highly unsatisfactory, however, imposing severe limitations on the kinds of simulation that can be attempted. It is often difficult even to distinguish between distortions introduced by the numerical methods and those resulting from deficiencies in the mathematical model. Thus the future will continue to present challenging and thorny problems in this field.

MATHEMATICAL SCIENCES IN ECONOMICS

The explicit penetration of nonelementary mathematics into economics began about a century ago with the introduction of rates of change in terms of marginal ratios and elasticities. For many decades, economists carried out derivations in words or graphical patterns rather than by formulas. These derivations did, of course, involve chains of symbolic reasoning and were thus intrinsically mathematical, though not always recognized as such. The twentieth century has seen a rapidly increasing use of formulas and of mathematical results and theorems (see the essay by Klein in reference 7). It has rather steadily been true that about half of the papers appearing in the principal economics journals would have been rejected ten years earlier as "too mathematical." The earlier uses of mathematics in economics centered around the use of the calculus as a means of describing interrelationships. The emphasis slowly changed to problems of maximization or minimization, originally of smoothly varying functions with no or few constraints.

Problems dealing with the appropriate behavior—that which rational participants "ought," or clients should be advised, to exhibit —were intermingled from an early date with problems concerning the effects of ideal mechanisms, such as free competition, in distributing goods and services. Both classes of problem involve optimizing allocation of resources. Today, the mathematics of optimized allocation, control, and decision, discussed in Chapter 5, has many applications in economics, and economists as well as mathematicians contribute to it.

Alongside mathematical economics is the very active area of econometrics, in which statistical tools, many of them developed for the purpose, are essential. Here, too, both economists and statisticians are contributing to the development of new techniques and to fresh understandings of old ones.

As in so many other areas, large parts of economics are being almost revolutionized by the availability of modern computing systems to store and digest quantities of data and to solve complex problems either directly or by tentative approximation.

Large areas of economics are now highly mathematized. For example, there are mathematical theorems concerning the existence of competitive economic equilibrium. The study of business cycles leads to systems of differential equations similar to those occurring in dynamics of physical systems. Indeed, many of the most respected economists are mathematically oriented. Key economists know as much of the details of modern control theory and what is known about the stability of nonlinear systems, to take two examples, as do all but the most specialized mathematicians. It is therefore not surprising that most members of the President's Council of Economic Advisers and its professional staff have been trained as mathematical economists. We recall also that J. M. Keynes, the father of modern economics, had been trained as a mathematician.

Education in economics is now highly mathematically oriented. In most major departments in the United States, all economics PhD's are required to learn calculus, selected topics in advanced calculus, the elements of linear algebra and probability, statistical inference, and econometrics. As a foundation for everyone, this is an impressive array, especially in contrast to the situation one, two, or three decades ago. In many leading graduate centers, additional mathematics courses are replacing the requirement of a second language for PhD candidates.

MATHEMATICS IN FINANCE AND INSURANCE

The vast majority of humanity uses elementary mathematics primarily in handling money. As a matter of fact, the reawakening of mathematics in Europe during the Renaissance coincides roughly with the transition from a barter economy to a monetary economy. The universal spread of rudimentary mathematical literacy was a concomitant of the development of that economy.

On a more sophisticated level, mathematics is used in insurance, in particular in life insurance, which dates back to the end of the sixteenth century. Statistical methods have been developed partly as a result of the needs of insurance companies. Mortality tables were among the first statistical tables published. The actuarial profession is a typical instance of a thoroughly mathematized technology. The flowering of mathematical statistics in Scandinavia during recent decades was certainly seeded by Scandinavian concern with the mathematics of insurance.

One of the more interesting applications of mathematics in actuarial work is the extraction of a set of mortality rates from observed data and the substitution of smoothly progressing rates for the irregular set extracted. This is the classical problem of graduation which has been attacked in many ways over the years, most recently within the framework of a Bayesian approach.

Among the early graduation methods employed by actuaries were various adaptations of curve-fitting. Later a number of linear compound formulas were devised to produce smoothly progressing rates, judged by the reduction of error in third differences. In recent years, the most widely used graduation formula has been one based on a difference equation, which represents a compromise between smoothness and closeness of fit. Within the last year, new graduation methods have been developed as a problem in straightforward statistical estimation of a large set of mortality rates simultaneously, proceeding, however, from a prior distribution of the "true" rates grounded on personal probability and making use of Bayes' theorem.

Another type of problem is illustrated by various elaborations of the theory of risk, which has been developed as a special case of the theory of stochastic processes. The so-called "collective risk theory" focuses attention on the distributions of total claims of an insurance company at the end of a specified period of time, so that a reasonable judgment might be made about appropriate limits of retention or bounds of acceptable adverse fluctuations. These are essential considerations in reinsurance.

Collective theory of risk was developed by a number of Scandinavian actuaries (notably F. Lundberg, H. Cramer, and C. O. Segerdahl) for investigating insurance company operations from a probabilistic viewpoint or, more realistically, the emergence of profits in a risk enterprise. The basic model considers the distribution of total claims of a risk enterprise as being composed of two elements —frequency and severity; the resulting distribution of total claims can be regarded as a stationary stochastic process with independent increments and as a compound Poisson process. In recent years, the fundamental assumptions of the theory, and hence its range of application, have been significantly enlarged by the use of more general probability models that allow for certain types of fluctuations in basic probabilities. The exact distribution of total claims of an insurance company has been studied analytically for a variety of assumptions. Ingenious numerical approximations have been developed, and more recent broader analytic-numerical studies of total claim distributions have been made, relying extensively on computer simulation.

MATHEMATICS IN MANAGEMENT AND OPERATIONS

During World War II, the use of simple mathematical models and mathematical thinking to study the conduct of military operations became a recognized art, as first scientists and later mathematicians, lawyers, and people with other backgrounds demonstrated its effectiveness. After the war, attempts to apply the same attitudes and approaches to business and industrial operations and management were pressed forward rather successfully. Combined with techniques and thinking drawn from, or suggested by, classical economics, this line of development has now led to an active field about whose names Howard Raiffa of Harvard University has observed:

Some names which are used more or less interchangeably are: Management Science, Operations Analysis, Operations Research, Decision Analysis, Systems Analysis, Cost–Benefit Analysis, Mathematical Programming (under certainty and under uncertainty), Decision and Control, Optimization Theory, Control Theory, Applied Mathematics II (Roman numeral I is reserved for mathematical physics and astronomy). Of course, researchers and practitioners in these areas could each argue persuasively that their title is most appropriate and that what they do is somewhat broader than what others do.

Whatever the title, the flavor of what is done is the same, combining the use of numerical data about operating experience so characteristic of early military applications with mathematical models to provide guidance for managerial action and judgment. This field was created by scientists accustomed to the use of mathematics; both its spirit and its techniques have always been thoroughly mathematical in character. This mathematical approach is steadily penetrating the practice of management and operation.

A number of the leading schools of business administration have concluded that mathematics is important both as a tool and as a language for management, and that training for the professional class of managers should include a substantial dose of this field of many names. Therefore, calculus, linear algebra, and computer programming either must be prerequisite for entrance or must be taken early in the graduate training program. At a leading business school (Harvard), which is not "mathematically oriented" and where no such requirements are imposed, about 75 percent of the entering students have at least two years of college mathematics, several elective courses requiring that degree of mathematical sophistication are given, and there is a sizable group of faculty members who have PhD degrees in mathematics or applied mathematics.

This field is pervasively mathematized and computerized, but it is far from being strictly a mathematical science. The pattern of its problems is frequently described as formulating the problem, constructing a mathematical model, deriving a solution from the model, testing the model and the solution, establishing control over the solution, and implementing the solution. Only one of the six steps is completely mathematical; the others involve the actual problem in an essential way. In these other steps, of course, there are many applications, some of them crucial, of statistics and computer science. The mathematical step, especially when dealing with management rather than operational problems, often draws on concepts and results from the field of optimized allocation, control, and decision.

A good practitioner combines the characteristics of most professional consulting and of most effective application of mathematics: abundant common sense, willingness to produce half-answers in a half-hour, recognition of his key roles as problem formulator and contributor to long-run profits (rather than as problem solver or researcher). Yet for all this, and in an alien environment, he must retain his skill as a mathematician.

CONCLUDING REMARKS

We have touched upon only some of the uses of mathematical methods in disciplines outside of the mathematical sciences proper. The number of such instances is steadily increasing, and the boundary lines between mathematical sciences and sciences that use mathematics are often difficult to draw.

The increasing use of mathematical methods in the biological sciences was pointed out earlier in the section on The Mathematization of Culture (see page 3); and the essay by Hirsh Cohen in reference 7 discusses in more detail a variety of biomedical applications of mathematics. A 1967 compilation by Thrall *et al.*[14] provides extensive further illustration of applications of mathematical models in biology.

An important omission in our discussion is the burgeoning field of mathematical psychology. A comprehensive survey of this field can be found in reference 13. Another important example of the penetration of mathematical methods into hitherto unmathematized areas is in the young science of mathematical linguistics, which applies mathematical methods and the mathematical way of thinking to the study of living languages. (See, for instance, the essay by Harris in reference 7.)

All great goods spawn small evils. Every new and powerful tool is misused as well as used wisely. This was true of printing and mechanical power when these tools were new. Today, in any field of endeavor where mathematics or statistics or computing is new, there will be those who use these tools inadvisedly, as a means of persuasion when the evidence is incomplete or even incorrect, or as a means of "blessing" conclusions that do not deserve support. All fields now well mathematized or well statisticized or well computerized have suffered through these difficulties. Those in process now, or to be in process in the near future, will have to suffer too. Such difficulties often slow down the incorporation of mathematics or statistics or computing into the heart of a new field of application. These delays are, we fear, inevitable.

The one antidote that has proved effective is an increased amount of mathematical or statistical or computing literacy for the majority of those who work in the field. This increase comes in two parts, separable but usually joined: on the one hand, enough literacy about the mathematics involved to understand the meaning, perhaps even the details, of the manipulations required; on the other, often even more important, an understanding of how mathematics or statistics or computing fits into actual problems in similar areas. This latter includes an appreciation of one of the skills of an effective user: the ability to be usually sound as to what must be taken into account in formal or numerical manipulations, what can probably be neglected, and what is surely negligible. It is not easy to teach these things explicitly; they are usually learned by experience in doing and thus come to depend on at least some facility with the manipulations concerned.

III

The Mathematical Sciences in Education

Research in the mathematical sciences is intimately connected with education. The overwhelming preponderance of basic mathematical research is done in universities by professors who view teaching and the guidance of research apprentices as an essential part of their intellectual lives. Graduate teaching in the mathematical sciences merges directly into doctoral and postdoctoral research guidance; and undergraduate education merges into graduate education, many graduate courses being open nowadays to qualified undergraduates.

There is, however, a more important reason why the present report should devote considerable attention to undergraduate as well as graduate education. For, as mathematical methods appear in an increasing variety of human activities, it is at the undergraduate level that there is the clearest prospect of greatly changing and increasing needs for mathematical courses among students in other fields. The implications of this for staff and curricula in the mathematical sciences are severe and are considered in detail below. *Our main conclusion is that there is now a shortage of qualified college teachers of the mathematical sciences, and that this situation is likely to get worse before it gets better.**

Undergraduate mathematical education in turn depends on mathematical training at the secondary and elementary school levels.

* *Added in proof:* All our estimates and predictions about future numbers of PhD's were formulated before the February 1968 issuance of new Selective Service rules affecting graduate students. If these rules should result in a serious depletion of the graduate student population, this would, of course, intensify the predicted shortage of PhD's in the mathematical sciences.

While it was early decided that it was beyond our scope to make a direct study of school-level mathematics and its curriculum reform movements, our studies have necessarily touched on school-level mathematics in two ways. First, we have had to recognize the effect on college mathematical curricula of the changing and generally improving preparation of entering college students. Second, we have had to take account of the increasing needs for higher mathematical education on the part of those who are or will become secondary or elementary school teachers.

The Lindquist and CBMS Surveys

For academic year 1960–1961, Clarence B. Lindquist of the U.S. Office of Education made a detailed and comprehensive survey[15] of U.S. higher education in the mathematical sciences. On the initiative of its Chairman, Gail S. Young, the Survey Committee of the Conference Board of the Mathematical Sciences (CBMS) has, with the assistance of Dr. Lindquist, repeated this survey for academic year 1965–1966, using a questionnaire very similar to Lindquist's for undergraduate education and separate detailed questionnaires for graduate education in mathematics, statistics, and computer science. Taken together, the Lindquist and CBMS studies yield trend information on mathematical education in the four-year colleges and universities of the United States in a depth and extensiveness hitherto unparalleled in studies of higher education for any academic field. The CBMS Survey Committee has now completed a similar survey, for academic year 1966–1967, of mathematical education in the two-year colleges (including technical institutes) in the United States. The CBMS Survey Committee is publishing the full results of its various studies in its own report.[16] Both the Lindquist and CBMS studies have been used extensively by COSRIMS and its Panels. For brevity we refer to these simply as the Lindquist survey and the CBMS survey.

7

Undergraduate Education

Mathematics departments in colleges and universities today serve a wide variety of student majors. They train future mathematical scientists, both for academic work and for work in industry and government, and, as it has for centuries, mathematical training plays a key role in the education of physical scientists and engineers. In recent years mathematical methods have proved to be of increasing use in the biological and social sciences as well, and so the mathematician is now acquiring another large group of clients. Secondary and elementary school teachers form yet another increasing contingent. Some knowledge of mathematics has traditionally been recognized as a significant part of the general education of a college student; today this knowledge is being broadened to include some appreciation of the widely useful tool of computers.

Chapter 3 of the report of our Panel on Undergraduate Education[1] surveys in detail these various components of demand for mathematical training; and, on this basis, Chapter 4 of that report makes an assessment of the resulting needs for college and university staff in the mathematical sciences. We give a briefer discussion along similar lines in the sections below, on total mathematical-science course enrollments and on quality and distribution of mathematical-science faculty.

The first thing to be emphasized about the recent history of undergraduate education in the mathematical sciences is the extent of its growth and change over the past 25 years. Our Panel on Undergraduate Education has documented this vividly in Chapter

121

2 of its report, presenting eight detailed case histories of changes at individual colleges and universities. While these institutions represent considerable variety in their educational goals and in their clientele, they reveal many similar trends over the last quarter century with regard to the mathematical sciences. The following items occur repeatedly: very significant increases in mathematics-course enrollments; spectacular increases in numbers of mathematics majors; new undergraduate major programs in the mathematical sciences; many new advanced courses; increased undergraduate enrollments in graduate courses; impact of improved high school curricula on beginning college mathematics courses; special new courses for statistics, computing, and the social sciences; significant increases in staff size; difficulties in recruiting new staff.

The Increase in Mathematics Majors

Perhaps the most striking item on the above list is the greatly increased number of mathematics majors. This is documented more precisely in Table 1, which shows comparative tabulations and projections* by K. A. Simon and M. G. Fullam of the U.S. Office of Education.[17]

These tabulations show that over the years 1955–1965, during which college enrollments roughly doubled, the annual number of bachelor's degrees granted in mathematics and statistics increased by a factor of 4.9, while for engineering, the physical sciences, and the biological sciences the corresponding factors were only 1.6, 1.7, and 2.8, respectively. The projections shown for the years 1965–1975 call for the annual number of bachelor's degrees in mathematics and statistics to increase by a factor of 3.0, while for engineering, the physical sciences, and the biological sciences the correspond-

---

* We have rounded off these projections to two significant figures, though, no doubt, for a year as remote as 1976 it is at most the initial figure that is at all likely to be borne out. The projections are based on the assumption that the percentage distribution of degrees by field will continue the 1955–1966 trends. This is, we feel, a reasonable basis for projections; but should it turn out to be only indifferently fulfilled, the projections could, of course, be even more in error. For instance, projections from the 1955–1959 trends on this basis would hardly have predicted the depression in numbers of engineering bachelor's degrees that actually occurred in the early 1960's, as shown in Table 1.

TABLE 1 Earned Bachelor's Degrees, 1955–1966, with Projections to 1976

YEAR	MATHEMATICS AND STATISTICS	ENGINEERING	PHYSICAL SCIENCES	BIOLOGICAL SCIENCES
EARNED, 1955–1966				
1954–1955	4,034	22,589	10,516	9,050
1955–1956	4,660	26,312	11,672	12,566
1956–1957	5,546	31,211	12,934	13,868
1957–1958	6,924	35,332	14,352	14,408
1958–1959	9,019	38,134	15,460	15,149
1959–1960	11,437	37,808	16,057	15,655
1960–1961	13,127	35,866	15,500	16,162
1961–1962	14,610	34,735	15,894	17,014
1962–1963	16,121	33,458	16,276	19,218
1963–1964	18,677	35,226	17,527	22,827
1964–1965	19,668	36,795	17,916	25,305
1965–1966	21,190	35,830	18,020	25,680
PROJECTED TO 1976				
1966–1967	24,000	37,000	19,000	28,000
1967–1968	31,000	43,000	23,000	33,000
1968–1969	36,000	45,000	24,000	37,000
1969–1970	38,000	44,000	26,000	38,000
1970–1971	41,000	43,000	27,000	39,000
1971–1972	45,000	44,000	28,000	41,000
1972–1973	49,000	44,000	30,000	44,000
1973–1974	55,000	45,000	31,000	47,000
1974–1975	60,000	46,000	33,000	50,000
1975–1976	65,000	46,000	35,000	53,000

ing projected factors of increase are 1.3, 1.9, and 2.0, respectively. Admittedly, projections can be no more than rough guides; and, in fact, discrepancies for 1965 between the above actual figures and the Office of Education's slightly earlier projected figures[18] suggest that the above projected factors of increase for 1965–1975 might turn out to be somewhat high for mathematics and statistics and somewhat low for the biological sciences. Even so, there seems little doubt that increased numbers of majors will contribute considerably to college staffing strains in the mathematical sciences over the next few years.

TOTAL ENROLLMENTS IN THE MATHEMATICAL SCIENCES

The Lindquist and CBMS surveys together show that over the period from academic years 1960–1961 to 1965–1966 the total enrollment in undergraduate mathematical-science courses increased from 744,000 to 1,068,000, or 44 percent. Since the most closely comparable general enrollment figures show a 48 percent increase over this same period, we conclude that for this period the growth in undergraduate mathematical-science enrollments has been roughly the same as the growth in college enrollments generally. (See reference 16.)

For the succeeding period from 1965–1966 to 1970–1971, however, we have reason to believe that this situation will change considerably. If the projections below, which are a more conservative version of those of our Undergraduate Panel, are at all near the mark, then mathematical-science enrollments will increase by more than 70 percent over this period, while general enrollments will increase by only around 30 percent. The remainder of this section presents the case for these projections.

For the academic year 1965–1966 the CBMS survey found that in the four-year colleges and universities of the United States there were some 1,068,000 undergraduate course enrollments in the mathematical sciences. For these colleges and universities, the U.S. Office of Education predicts[17] a 29 percent rise in total undergraduate enrollments over the period 1965–1970. Thus, taking 29 percent of 1,068,000, one might predict a rise over this period of approximately 310,000 undergraduate course enrollments in the mathematical sciences. We believe this to be a serious underestimate because of two factors. The first of these factors is the projected faster-than-average growth in the number of majors in certain fields where it is customary to take a greater-than-average amount of mathematical course work. The second is the fact that majors in several fields are now beginning to take more courses in the mathematical sciences than formerly and by 1970 will almost surely be taking significantly more such courses on the average than in 1965.

Chapter 4 of the report of our Panel on Undergraduate Education[1] has analyzed, for each of the principal fields concerned, the extent to which one or both of these factors may be expected to increase mathematical-science course enrollments over the 1965–1970 period, above and beyond the 310,000 attributable to the gen-

TABLE 2 Projected Mathematical-Science Course-Enrollment Increase, 1965–1970

FACTOR	INCREASE
General growth	310,000
Mathematical-sciences excess	81,300
Physical-sciences excess	37,000
Engineering excess	37,000
Biological-sciences excess	19,500
Psychology excess	12,500
Social-sciences excess	67,500
Elementary-teacher excess	60,000
Introductory-computing excess	172,000
TOTAL	796,800

eral 29 percent growth predicted for college enrollments over this period. This analysis is based on the following: (1) the U.S. Office of Education projections[17] regarding the number of bachelor's degrees to be expected in various fields in 1970; (2) information from the CBMS survey regarding the average number of mathematical-science courses taken by majors in these various fields as of 1965; and (3) the Committee on the Undergraduate Program in Mathematics (CUPM) panel recommendations,[19–23] as an indication of the number of mathematical-science courses to be reasonably anticipated for majors in these various fields by 1970.

We and our Panel on Undergraduate Education are very much aware of the oversimplifications and possibilities for error involved in making, for several years ahead, any course-enrollment projections whatever. For this reason, the Panel on Undergraduate Education has, in Chapter 4 of its report, considered the consequences of varying its projected data and its hypotheses in several reasonable ways. The prediction of intensification, for several years to come, of the shortage of qualified college teachers of the mathematical sciences is found to be stable under all these variations. Our own figures, shown in Table 2, provide a further variation. It too predicts an intensified shortage in the supply of qualified teachers over the next few years. It is for these reasons that we feel some confidence in this prediction.

With these qualifications and reservations, we present, in Table 2, our best effort to project mathematical-science course-enrollment increases from 1965 to 1970. The first item in this tabulation is the one mentioned earlier: the basic 310,000 increase in mathematical-science course enrollments to be anticipated simply from the U.S. Office of Education's prediction of a 29 percent general increase in college enrollments.

For the mathematical sciences, the physical sciences, and engineering, the projected excesses shown in Table 2 are those computed by our Panel on Undergraduate Education. The mathematical-sciences excess arises from the more rapid growth in mathematical-science majors already discussed, together with the fact that such a major accounts for approximately six course enrollments in his field during his undergraduate years. The physical-sciences excess arises from two factors: first, a higher-than-average projected rise in the number of majors, who in 1965 typically took approximately three mathematical-science courses during their undergraduate years; and second, the prediction, based on reference 23, that by 1970 these majors will be taking four rather than three such courses. For engineering, the projected 1965–1970 increase in majors is at 21 percent instead of the general figure of 29 percent, which by itself would yield a deficiency rather than an excess in mathematical-science course enrollments; but this deficiency is more than offset by the tendency, already beginning to be seen, for the undergraduate engineering curriculum to shift from a five-semester to a seven-semester sequence in the mathematical sciences (see reference 24).

For the biological sciences, psychology, and the social sciences, the figures shown in Table 2 are just half as large as those in the report of the Panel on Undergraduate Education. Our figures correspond to the assumption that, on the average, by 1970 *half* of the majors in these fields will be taking, during their undergraduate careers, one more mathematical-science course than was typical for the majors in these fields in 1965. (The Panel on Undergraduate Education made the assumption that by 1970 *all* majors in these fields would on the average be taking one more such course.)

With regard to elementary school teachers, we recognize that a strong movement is already under way to stimulate the upgrading of their preservice training in mathematics. The cupm report[23] and regional conferences of elementary teachers sponsored by the cupm[25] have done much in this respect. As a result, we feel that, on the average, perhaps two thirds of these teachers will by 1970 be taking one more mathematics course during their undergraduate years than in 1965 (whereas the Panel on Undergraduate Education felt it likely that, on the average, *all* elementary teachers would be taking one more such course by 1970).

It is particularly difficult to make predictions regarding the rapidly growing and changing field of computing. The recently published Pierce report[3] recommends that by academic year 1970–1971 *all* college students should have an introductory course in computing. It may turn out that the ideal place for such an introductory course is in high school rather than college; or it may turn out that introductory computing courses oriented toward various subject-matter fields will tend to be taught in various college departments, much as elementary applied statistics courses tend to be today. The most likely assumption, however, seems to be that the burden of teaching such courses will fall on the college faculty in computer science and the mathematical sciences generally. In any event, our Panel on Undergraduate Education has made its projections on the assumption that half of the 5,500,000 undergraduates in four-year colleges in 1970 will take, at some time during their four-year undergraduate careers, a one-semester college course in computing, and that half of these are not already included elsewhere in the tabulation in Table 2. (This last is certainly not unreasonable in view of the present distribution of college majors.) This yields the equivalent of about 172,000 (academic-year) course enrollments for 1970, and it is this figure that appears in Table 2.

Table 2 yields a total projected course-enrollment increase of 796,800. Dividing this by the course-enrollment total of 1,068,000 for academic year 1965–1966, we find that, over the 1965–1970 period, mathematical-science course enrollments are projected to increase by approximately 74 percent, which is more than 2.5 times the 29 percent by which general college enrollments are projected to increase over this period.

QUALITY AND DISTRIBUTION OF MATHEMATICAL-SCIENCE FACULTY

The CBMS survey found that for the four-year colleges and universities of the United States the 1,068,000 undergraduate mathematical-course enrollments of academic year 1965–1966 were handled by a full-time faculty of some 10,750, aided by a quite small part-time faculty and, in universities, graduate assistants. This yields a ratio of one full-time faculty member to approximately 100 course en-

TABLE 3   Highest Earned Degree, 1965–1966

DEGREE	NUMBER
Doctorate (mathematical sciences)	5,000
Doctorate (education)	500
Doctorate (other fields)	200
Master's degree	4,650
Bachelor's degree	400
TOTAL	10,750

rollments. Now the preceding section estimated some 796,800 more course enrollments in the mathematical sciences for academic year 1970–1971 than for academic year 1965–1966. Therefore, this course-enrollment increase will require some 8,000 more full-time faculty in the mathematical sciences for academic year 1970–1971 than for academic year 1965–1966.

We now try to assess what the quality of the additional faculty is likely to be, using as a rough measure of faculty quality the proportion of full-time faculty holding doctorates, as is done in Cartter's studies.[26],* For academic year 1965–1966, the CBMS survey found the 10,750 full-time faculty in the mathematical sciences to have highest earned degrees distributed as shown in Table 3. Thus in academic year 1965–1966 some 53 percent of the mathematical-science faculty held doctorates in some field, a little over 46

* Academic degree is, of course, only one dimension in the measure of quality. It is clear, for instance, that one is qualified to provide instruction in a core mathematics topic only if he has a thorough grasp of the substantive material of that topic, of its relation to mathematics at large, and of the manner in which others will build upon the foundation it provides. By the same token, one is qualified to provide instruction on a facet of the *use* of mathematics only if (again) he has a thorough grasp of the mathematical disciplines he must use, of the facets of science or technology under study, and of the attitudes and objectives that are appropriate to the questions with which he is coping. Thus, not only must there be an adequate level of competence as measured by academic degree acquisition, but there must also be a breadth of topical competence measured in terms of ranges of interest, attitudes, and scientific literacy.

Clearly, in institutions that are only beginning to develop comprehensive programs, these requirements of quality cannot be met immediately, but they should be used as guidelines for that development. A minimum first step requires that the means be found to assist faculty members to maintain contact with the changes in relevant fields of knowledge.

percent being in the mathematical sciences. Shortly we shall discuss the distribution of doctorate-holding faculty among colleges and universities, which is far from uniform.

To see how the percentage of doctorates is likely to change over the next few years, we now need an estimate of the number of new PhD's who will enter mathematical-science teaching in four-year colleges and universities over the period 1965–1970. For this we take the estimate of our Panel on Undergraduate Education, which found this number to be approximately 3,300 (see Chapter 4 of their report[1]). Their analysis followed Cartter's model[27] and used his figure of 2 percent per year for attrition (due to death, retirement, and net outflow to other professions) of doctorate holders from college and university teaching. Also, in accord with information from the CBMS survey, they assumed that 70 percent of the newly produced mathematical-science PhD's will go into college and university teaching, as opposed to Cartter's value of approximately 33 percent for all academic fields combined.*

To collect our figures, we have estimated that over the period 1965–1970 some 8,000 new full-time staff members will be needed in mathematical-science teaching in the four-year colleges and universities. We also have the estimate of net inflow of some 3,300 PhD's into such teaching during this period. Thus only about 41 percent of the new faculty will have doctorates; hence, if these estimates are at all close, the percentage of doctorate holders on mathematical-science faculties, currently about 53 percent, will decline.

The distribution of the doctorate-holding faculty is far from uniform, the universities having more than twice the fraction of the total doctorate-holding faculty that liberal arts and teachers' colleges have, while the latter carry slightly more of the total undergraduate teaching load. Specifically, the CBMS survey reveals that for academic year 1965–1966 the distribution of doctorate-holding faculty was approximately that shown in Table 4, which should be read with the following comments in mind.

First, it is not surprising that the universities have a much higher

---

* With the strong demand from other quarters, it is a distinct possibility that in the future fewer than 70 percent of the new PhD's will go into academic work. This could intensify the college teacher shortage predicted here. In any case, it should be emphasized that the prediction of a growing shortage is stable under any reasonable variation in the particular percentages used for attrition and for new PhD's entering teaching.

TABLE 4   Distribution of Doctorate-Holding Faculty, 1965–1966

TYPE OF INSTITUTION	PERCENTAGE OF THE UNDERGRADUATE TEACHING LOAD	PERCENTAGE OF THE DOCTORATE-HOLDING FACULTY
Universities	45	63
Liberal arts and teachers' colleges	49	30
Technological institutes	6	7
TOTALS	100	100

fraction of a limited doctorate-holding faculty, since it is universities that carry the bulk of graduate instruction and the direction of doctoral and postdoctoral research. Second, as far as the first two undergraduate years are concerned, the proportion of PhD's teaching at universities is much more closely comparable with that at liberal arts colleges and teachers' colleges, because of the wide employment of graduate assistants in such teaching at universities. In this connection, the CBMS survey has found that, in the median university, 40 percent of the freshman–sophomore teaching load is carried by graduate assistants, and, in 38 percent of the universities, at least half of the freshman–sophomore load is carried in this way.

In Chapter 8, we discuss (see page 145) Graduate Student Participation in Undergraduate Teaching in universities and suggest improvements for the future. In Chapter 9, in the discussion of The College Teacher (page 147), we consider what may be done to meet anticipated shortages in qualified faculty in the mathematical sciences, especially in the weaker colleges and in certain critical fields.

The Junior Colleges

There are now more entering freshmen in junior colleges than in universities, and over one third of all entering freshmen are junior college students. This statement is impressive even when it is understood that the term "junior colleges" here includes two-year technical institutes, and that the data include part-time students and students in occupational or general studies programs not chiefly creditable toward a bachelor's degree. The actual figures, from the U.S. Office of Education,[28] are shown in Table 5. Total enrollment

TABLE 5   First-Time Enrollments in Fall 1966, Nondegree Credit and Part-Time Students Included

	NUMBER (THOUSANDS OF STUDENTS)	PERCENTAGE OF TOTAL
Universities	427	27
Other four-year institutions	591	38
Two-year institutions	547	35
TOTALS	1,565	100

figures with a breakdown into full-time and part-time students are also instructive and are given in Table 6. These figures show that in 1966 two-year institutions accounted for 21 percent of all undergraduate enrollments, 17 percent of the full-time ones, and 30 percent of the part-time ones.

Enrollments in junior colleges are geographically heavily concentrated in certain states, reflecting not only differences in population density but also differences in state policy regarding the establishment and expansion of these institutions. Thus 38 percent of all junior college students are in California, and slightly over 50 percent attend junior colleges in California, Florida, or Illinois.

Against this background of general student enrollments we now give a few results from the 1966–1967 CBMS survey of the mathe-

TABLE 6   Total Enrollments in Fall 1966, Nondegree Credit and Part-Time Students Included[a]

	THOUSANDS OF STUDENTS		
	TOTAL	FULL-TIME	PART-TIME
Universities	2,482	1,789	693
Other four-year institutions	2,626	1,941	685
Two-year institutions	1,331	739	591
All institutions	6,439	4,469	1,969

[a]Figures from reference 20.

TABLE 7 Distribution of Mathematical-Science Course Enrollments in Fall 1966, by Size of Junior College

INSTITUTIONAL SIZE (NO. OF STUDENTS)	NO. OF COURSE ENROLLMENTS	DISTRIBUTION (%)
5,000 and over	107,000	31
2,000 to 4,999	104,000	30
1,000 to 1,999	55,000	16
Under 1,000	82,000	23
All institutions	348,000	100

matical sciences in junior colleges, the first such survey ever made. A much more thorough presentation and discussion appears in the CBMS Survey Committee's report,[16] Volume I, Chapter V. Numbers of mathematical-science course enrollments, broken down according to the size of the institution, are given in Table 7.

Enrollments of entering freshmen in mathematics courses tend to be at less advanced levels for junior colleges than for four-year colleges, as Table 8 shows. In the junior colleges of largest enrollment (over 5,000), 55 percent of all mathematics course enrollments by entering freshmen for the fall of 1966 were below the level of college algebra and trigonometry. While junior college freshmen tended to have a generally lower attainment level in high school mathematics, the differences shown in Table 8 appear to reflect not so much differences in ability as differences in goals. A considerable

TABLE 8 Percentage Distribution of Entering Freshmen Enrollments at Three Mathematics Course Levels

LEVEL	TWO-YEAR INSTITUTIONS, FALL 1966	FOUR-YEAR INSTITUTIONS, FALL 1965
Below college algebra and trigonometry	42%	19%
College algebra, trigonometry, and equivalent	44%	49%
Analytic geometry, calculus, and above	14%	33%

fraction—perhaps 30 percent—of the junior college students aim for immediate occupations in business and technology rather than for careers in teaching or other professions. (Most of the remaining 70 percent are students intending to transfer to four-year colleges upon graduation.)

Among junior college students, those in occupational curricula have mathematical needs and abilities somewhat different from those intending to transfer to four-year colleges. Some of the strongly occupation-oriented mathematics is, in fact, taught outside mathematics departments altogether. The most common example of this is business mathematics taught in a division of business. Other examples are precalculus technical mathematics and statistics.

It is to be emphasized that industry needs technical aides who are graduates of strong two-year college programs. In fact, a spokesman for a prominent industrial laboratory has indicated that although salaries and opportunities for advancement are good, well-trained technical aides are often harder for industry to find in needed numbers than are those with more advanced professional training.

The Mathematics Faculty in Junior Colleges

In junior colleges in 1967, the full-time mathematical-science faculty numbered approximately 2,700; and taking into account part-time faculty members, the full-time equivalent faculty was approximately 3,100. Their training was overwhelmingly at the master's level: 84 percent had the master's as their highest degree, 12 percent the bachelor's, and about 4 percent the doctorate. The field of highest level of training was within the mathematical sciences for only 62 percent; for 24 percent it was mathematics education, and for 14 percent it was in some other field.

To the question, "Do you have difficulty in recruiting and keeping an adequate mathematics faculty?" about 73 percent of the junior college mathematics departments responding to the CBMS questionnaire said, somewhat surprisingly, that they did *not*. Probably the principal reason for this is that the better high school teachers form an enormous and highly available pool of supply. Another reason is that, even in comparison with the private four-year colleges, the public junior colleges can offer a better median salary to professors.

Whether this faculty is indeed adequate, and whether it will prove adequate for the future, may be questioned. The Mathematical Association of America, in its resolutions to the Congress and the National Science Foundation,[4] states that the junior colleges appear to form the weakest link in the chain of higher education in mathematics. Certainly a junior college teacher now qualified to teach only the most elementary mathematics courses may in the future find nothing he can teach; for the preparation of entering freshmen will undoubtedly continue to improve, and remedial teaching will increasingly be done by such techniques as programmed instruction. In its recent report,[29] an *ad hoc* CUPM Panel on the Qualification of College Teachers of Mathematics states that a strong mathematics master's degree (what it calls the "first graduate component") ". . . should represent adequate training for teaching transfer students in junior colleges, provided the teacher continues to remain intellectually alive." Although there are no firm percentages, many with experience gained in teaching-institute programs for college teachers feel that numerous junior college teachers with master's degrees fail to meet these criteria (see reference 16, Chapter 5).

In summary, the junior colleges form a fast-growing but geographically highly nonhomogeneous component of higher education. In these colleges, a strong and continuing effort will be needed to raise and maintain faculty professional standards in the mathematical sciences. The university mathematical community can contribute to this in two ways, primarily: first, by producing new junior college faculty with strong mathematical training through the master's level; and, second, by providing opportunities for appropriately oriented continuing education for those already doing mathematical-science teaching in junior colleges. The first of these ways underlines the fact that there is need for federal support for graduate mathematical training that stops at the master's level, as well as for PhD training. The second is a part of the effort in continuing mathematical education for college teachers, both academic-year training and summer training. This too will require strong federal support.

8

Graduate Education

The mathematical sciences have shared in the general accelerated growth that has marked graduate education in all the sciences since the late 1940's. Especially at the level of training for the doctorate, the United States has made impressive gains in the quality of its mathematical education. This has been reflected in increased international recognition of the research accomplishments of American-trained American mathematicians (see the section on The Position of the United States in Mathematics, page 10). It would also be widely agreed by professionals in the field that the number of truly distinguished university centers for mathematical research in the United States has roughly tripled during the postwar period, from approximately three to approximately nine (see Appendix E).

While U.S. graduate mathematical education has been growing in quality, it has also been growing in breadth. This is reflected in a broader span of courses and areas for research, as well as in the increasing election of graduate courses in the mathematical sciences by majors from other fields. It is also reflected in the creation and growth of new academically oriented professional societies in the mathematical sciences. In the early 1930's, there were just three such professional societies: The American Mathematical Society at the graduate and research level, the Mathematical Association of America at the collegiate level, and the National Council of Teachers of Mathematics at the secondary and elementary school levels. Increased interest in mathematical logic, a border area between mathematics and philosophy, led to the founding of the Association for Symbolic Logic in 1934. The Institute of Mathematical Statistics followed in 1935. During the postwar period, new applications of mathematics and new mathematical tools and techniques (see Chapters 5 and 6) resulted in the formation of four new professional societies in the mathematical sciences: The Society for Industrial and Applied Mathematics, the Association for Computing Machinery, the Operations Research Society of America, and The Institute of Management Sciences. In addition, today there exists an organization, the Conference Board of the Mathematical Sciences, which comprises most of the professional societies in the field and constitutes a medium through which their representatives can meet for exchange of information and discussion of problems of common concern.

THE MASTER'S DEGREE

Corresponding to Table 1 (see page 123) for bachelor's degrees, we present in Table 9 the comparative figures of the U.S. Office of Education[17] for numbers of master's degrees awarded in mathematics and statistics, engineering, the physical sciences, and the biological sciences during the period 1955–1966, with projections* to 1976.

As in the case of bachelor's degrees, the annual number of master's degrees granted shows a much greater factor of gain over the years 1955–1965 for mathematics and statistics (5.6) than for engineering (2.7), the physical sciences (1.9), or the biological sciences (2.2). The same is true of the factors of gain projected for 1965–1975: for mathematics and statistics this is 3.5, while for engineering, the physical sciences, and the biological sciences these projected factors are 2.6, 2.1, and 2.3, respectively. The projected factor of increase that Table 9 yields for mathematics and statistics may be high, because the assumption on which it is based, that the percentage distribution of degrees by field will continue the 1955–1965 trends, may not be completely fulfilled. On the other hand, the category "mathematics and statistics," which for the period 1955–1965 included virtually all the degrees of that period in the mathematical sciences, may miss significant numbers of these degrees in the period 1965–1975, especially degrees granted in the rapidly proliferating graduate departments of computer science.

It is clear that the standards and requirements for the master's

---

* Rounded by us to two significant figures. See footnote on page 122.

TABLE 9   Earned Master's Degrees, 1955–1966, with Projections to 1976

YEAR	MATHEMATICS AND STATISTICS	ENGINEERING	PHYSICAL SCIENCES	BIOLOGICAL SCIENCES
EARNED, 1955–1966				
1954–1955	761	4,484	2,544	1,609
1955–1956	892	4,724	2,653	1,754
1956–1957	965	5,233	2,704	1,801
1957–1958	1,234	5,788	3,034	1,852
1958–1959	1,509	6,753	3,202	2,007
1959–1960	1,765	7,159	3,387	2,154
1960–1961	2,238	8,178	3,799	2,358
1961–1962	2,680	8,909	3,929	2,642
1962–1963	3,323	9,635	4,132	2,921
1963–1964	3,603	10,827	4,567	3,297
1964–1965	4,294	12,056	4,918	3,604
1965–1966	5,220	13,990	5,470	4,390
PROJECTED TO 1976				
1966–1967	5,900	15,000	5,800	4,600
1967–1968	6,400	16,000	6,000	4,700
1968–1969	7,400	18,000	6,500	5,200
1969–1970	9,300	22,000	7,800	6,300
1970–1971	11,000	25,000	8,800	6,900
1971–1972	12,000	26,000	8,900	7,100
1972–1973	13,000	27,000	9,200	7,400
1973–1974	14,000	29,000	9,800	7,900
1974–1975	15,000	31,000	10,000	8,200
1975–1976	17,000	34,000	11,000	8,800

degree vary widely, though too little is known about this in a comprehensive way. In some departments, a master's degree is awarded simply upon the completion of a specified amount of course work beyond the bachelor's degree; sometimes the passing of comprehensive examinations (written, oral, or both) is required; in some programs a master's thesis is required; and in some departments a master's degree is awarded as a kind of "consolation prize" to those who try and fail to complete the requirements for a doctorate. For the mathematical sciences, about 60 percent of the master's degrees currently being awarded are granted by departments of mathematics that also offer a doctorate, and for these departments the CBMS survey furnishes a bit more information. Of the students admitted to study toward graduate degrees in such departments in the fall of 1965, the department expected about 51 percent to get only mathematics master's degrees, about 12 percent to get only master's degrees in the teaching of mathematics, and about 37 percent to get doctoral degrees. Of the last group, roughly half already had master's degrees. At about one fourth of these departments a thesis is definitely required for a master's degree; at about one half there are two alternative master's programs, one involving a thesis and one not; at the others no thesis is required, the requirement tending to consist of course work plus various kinds of comprehensive examinations. On the average, about one full year of course work is required for a master's degree in the mathematical sciences, and the median elapsed time from bachelor's to master's degree is between one and two years.

Many of those studying only for the master's degree are preparing to be mathematics teachers at the high school level. Though high school teachers usually teach more than one subject, it has been estimated that those high school teachers whose primary responsibility is mathematics teaching currently number approximately 120,000; and of these perhaps as many as 20 percent have master's degrees either in mathematics or in the teaching of mathematics. In addition, some mathematics MA's will certainly continue to find teaching positions in four-year colleges and universities. As we have seen (Table 3, page 128), in 1965 some 4,650, or 43 percent, of the full-time faculty of 10,750 in such institutions had the master's degree as their highest earned degree. Junior colleges offer a still small but fast-growing field of opportunity for those with mathematical training through the master's level. In the fall of 1966, according to the CBMS survey, there were about 2,700 mathematics teachers in junior colleges, of whom 84 percent, or 2,300, had master's degrees. (About 4 percent had doctorates, and the other 12 percent had bachelor's degrees.) Those employed by industry or government whose major educational field was mathematics now probably number well over 30,000 (see references 30 and 31); and of these approximately one quarter have master's degrees as their highest earned degree (see reference 31, page 22).

THE DOCTORATE IN THE MATHEMATICAL SCIENCES

As we have seen, the annual number of bachelor's degrees and the annual number of master's degrees showed much stronger gains

TABLE 10   Earned Doctor's Degrees, 1955–1966, with Projections to 1976

YEAR	MATHEMATICS AND STATISTICS	ENGINEERING	PHYSICAL SCIENCES	BIOLOGICAL SCIENCES
EARNED, 1955–1966				
1954–1955	250	599	1,713	994
1955–1956	235	610	1,667	1,025
1956–1957	249	596	1,674	1,103
1957–1958	247	647	1,655	1,125
1958–1959	282	714	1,812	1,045
1959–1960	303	786	1,838	1,205
1960–1961	344	943	1,991	1,193
1961–1962	396	1,207	2,122	1,338
1962–1963	490	1,378	2,380	1,455
1963–1964	596	1,693	2,455	1,625
1964–1965	688	2,124	2,829	1,928
1965–1966	770	2,350	2,960	2,030
PROJECTED TO 1976				
1966–1967	860	2,700	3,100	2,100
1967–1968	900	3,100	3,500	2,400
1968–1969	1,100	3,600	3,900	2,700
1969–1970	1,200	4,000	4,000	2,700
1970–1971	1,300	4,100	4,000	2,700
1971–1972	1,400	4,600	4,200	2,900
1972–1973	1,800	5,700	5,000	3,400
1973–1974	2,000	6,600	5,600	3,800
1974–1975	2,100	6,900	5,500	3,800
1975–1976	2,200	7,300	5,600	3,800

over the period 1955–1965 for mathematics and statistics than for engineering, the physical sciences, or the biological sciences; and the same was true to a more moderate extent of the projected gain factors for the period 1965–1975. For doctoral degrees the corresponding statistics and projections* of the U.S. Office of Education,[17] shown in Table 10, do not show any such decisively stronger gains for mathematics and statistics. The factors of gain in these numbers of doctoral degrees for the period 1955–1965 are: mathematics and statistics, 2.8; engineering, 3.6; physical sciences, 1.7; and biological sciences, 1.9. For the period 1965–1975 the corresponding

* Rounded by us to two significant figures. See footnote on page 122.

projected factors are: mathematics and statistics, 3.0; engineering, 3.2; physical sciences, 1.9; and biological sciences, 2.0.

For doctoral degrees, then, it is engineering, and not mathematics and statistics, that shows the highest factors of gain. While these gain factors are higher for mathematics and statistics than for the physical or biological sciences, the "conversion factor" from master's degree to doctorate is lower. Allowing for a time lag of two to four years between receipt of the master's and doctoral degrees, we can compare the total masters production over a period (Table 9) with the total PhD production over a similar period (Table 10) three years later. When this is done, the following conversion factors are obtained, representing the approximate percentage of masters in a ten-year period who go on to get a doctorate three years later:

Mathematics and statistics	30%
Physical sciences	80%
Biological sciences	73%

Without better knowledge than we have of the flow of students through various degree levels and into various occupations, we can account only speculatively and tentatively for this relatively small conversion factor for mathematics and statistics. One reason for it appears to be the very considerable proportion—quite a large majority—of mathematics graduate students working only for the master's degree, many of them studying to be teachers. As noted above in our discussion of the master's degree, even in mathematics departments offering the PhD degree this currently amounts to approximately 63 percent of those studying for graduate degrees; and presumably it includes a much larger percentage of those studying in graduate mathematics departments in which only a master's degree is offered. Another reason may be simply that doing research acceptable for the PhD degree is harder in mathematics than in other fields, leading fewer to try for this degree in mathematics and leading to a higher attrition rate among those who do. Research for the PhD degree in mathematics has traditionally meant the discovery of new mathematics, as contrasted with the scholarly synthesis of previous work often found in the humanities or the obtaining of new experimental results by established techniques often found in the laboratory sciences.

THE DOCTORATE OF PHILOSOPHY AND INTERMEDIATE DEGREES

For academic fields generally, questions have been raised concerning the relevance of the PhD degree for college teaching [see, e.g., E. Walters and F. W. Ness, "The Ph.D.: New Demands, Same Old Response," *Saturday Review, 49,* 62 (January 15, 1966)]. Alternative programs and doctorates have from time to time been proposed (notably, in the mathematical sciences, an expository-thesis program leading to a proposed "Doctor of Arts" degree), but these have received little support. Our Panel on Graduate Education has given careful consideration to the PhD and intermediate degrees in mathematics as degrees for college teachers. The following discussion is based closely on their report.

The PhD degree in the mathematical sciences has a unique value for university and college teachers in this field. Mathematics and its applications cannot be learned passively—that is, not merely by listening, reading, and studying. It is only by doing substantial problems, that is, by a genuine apprenticeship in research, that a graduate student can really absorb the mathematical way of thinking. The writing of a PhD thesis is an exciting and important phase in the development of a mathematician. He is at last functioning as a professional and not merely as a student. He realizes the difficulties, frustrations, and sheer hard work that the creation of mathematics requires and so will view with deeper insight the efforts of his colleagues to do mathematics. His sense of participation as a contributor to his subject will give him a greater authority and involvement as a teacher. The attainment of a PhD degree is an excellent scheme for making students gain the insight that comes from doing research. This insight is more important than ever now that purely routine use of mathematics is becoming totally inadequate for applications in other fields. For all these reasons it is highly desirable that, wherever possible, mathematical-science faculty members in universities and colleges should have the PhD degree in their field. (Compare the statement on the role of the PhD as discussed in reference 29.)

There are, of course, quite a few universities in which all, or virtually all, the full-time faculty members of the mathematics department do have PhD degrees. These would certainly include the 25 universities with mathematics departments rated as "excellent" or "strong" in over-all faculty quality listed on page 66 of Cartter's study.[32] As far as such universities are concerned, there have quite recently been indications of "saturation at the top," reflected in the fact that young mathematics PhD's of high ability and research promise are, in increasing numbers, finding positions in a broader range of universities. This means that the time is ripe for systematically developing excellence in more mathematics departments through such programs as the National Science Foundation's Science Development Programs (see the discussion of Developmental Block and Area Grants on page 174).

In the country's colleges and universities in general, however, the problems of providing adequate numbers of PhD faculty in the mathematical sciences seem overwhelmingly severe. The CBMS survey has determined that, as of 1966, over 70 percent of the liberal arts colleges and teachers' colleges—institutions that together carry nearly half of the undergraduate teaching load—had mathematical-science faculties with at most one PhD member, while over 40 percent had mathematical-science faculties with no PhD members.

In the face of this situation, the Committee on the Undergraduate Program in Mathematics has discussed and evaluated several lower levels of preparation in its report, *Qualifications for a College Faculty in Mathematics.*[29] It concludes that a teacher with what it calls the "Advanced Graduate Component" has the subject-matter background to teach all the undergraduate mathematics except specialized courses intended for students who are going to be research mathematicians. This Advanced Graduate Component is essentially the present-day training for the PhD degree except for the thesis. A student so trained at a university with a strong doctoral program will have participated for several years in the life of a research department; he is likely to have absorbed some of the research atmosphere and will therefore be less narrow in his interests and ultimately a better teacher than a student who has taken only a minimal master's degree. Moreover, he could complete this level of training and enter teaching in less time than he would require to complete his PhD degree.

Discussions with representatives of four-year colleges (see, e.g., reports of CUPM regional conferences[33]) show that many colleges would welcome teachers with the Advanced Graduate Component. Indeed, there have been suggestions even from the universities that, for undergraduates, the teacher who is excited about mathematics and teaches creatively, even if he does not have the PhD degree, is sometimes to be preferred to a teacher who holds a PhD degree.

For example, R. L. Wilder, in his paper "The Role of Intuition" [*Science, 156,* 605 (May 5, 1967)], says:

As the student goes on to more advanced work, the intuitive component of his training begins to assume more importance. At this stage of his career it may be assumed that he is possibly going on to do some kind of creative work, if not in mathematics, then in some other science. And it is desirable that his teachers have had some experience with creative work. This does not mean that the teacher must have a Ph.D. degree; this is a fetish I wish we could get rid of. I would much prefer a teacher without a Ph.D. who is excited about mathematics and can teach creatively, than a teacher with a Ph.D. who is neither enthusiastic about mathematics nor capable of inspiring his students.

Two questions now need to be answered. First, how many graduate students in the mathematical sciences stop their training at the level of the Advanced Graduate Component? Second, should this level of training be recognized in some formal way; and if so, in what way? There are no clear-cut answers to either question, but some reasonable guesses and comments can be made.

Estimates based on the general study, *Attrition of Graduate Students at the Ph.D. Level in the Traditional Arts and Sciences,*[34] suggest that, on the average, for every 100 PhD's produced there are perhaps 15 dropouts who will have reached the Advanced Graduate Component stage. Thus, corresponding to the approximately 800 PhD's per year currently produced in the mathematical sciences, there are perhaps 120 who stop at the Advanced Graduate Component level. It seems likely that this number could be considerably increased, if it seems desirable to do so, by offering intermediate degrees to students who are enthusiastic about mathematics but either lack the talent for original research or, possessing this talent only to a moderate extent, are not lucky enough to find supervisors who can help them develop it to the research-thesis level. On the other hand, it may be guessed that the present number of students (perhaps 120 a year) who complete PhD programs except for the thesis would not be greatly increased if an intermediate degree were generally available; it might rise to 200 or 300 a year at the most.

As for the question of formal recognition of the Advanced Graduate Component level of training, there is widespread agreement in the mathematical community that training to this level should be formally recognized in some way beyond the mere award of the master's degree. According to the CBMS survey, about 70 percent of the mathematics departments that grant the PhD degree are of this opinion. Indeed, several distinguished universities (for example, Yale and Michigan) have recently instituted such degrees. The existence of an intermediate degree would certainly make it easier to assess the quality of a prospective teacher or of a college faculty.

It is a much more controversial question whether an intermediate degree should be called a doctorate of some kind. The research thesis has been a traditional requirement for a doctorate in the mathematical sciences in the United States. Many people feel that it is dishonest to let a degree without such a thesis be called a doctorate, and thus to acquire a measure of the prestige that is justly associated with the present PhD degree in the mathematical sciences. A number of colleges have difficulty in giving permanent employment to teachers if they do not have doctorates. From one point of view, of course, this is a good thing, since it tends to prevent the development of a large body of college teachers who permanently occupy positions that might otherwise come to be occupied by younger and more highly qualified ones. It has also been argued that it would be dangerous to provide an easy alternative to the PhD degree, since many students might then be satisfied with it and so would miss the valuable experience of writing a thesis.

On the other hand, there are also strong arguments for recognizing the Advanced Graduate Component as a doctorate. The most significant one is precisely that college administrations are reluctant to grant tenure and status to teachers who do not have doctorates. As pointed out earlier, the best available projections indicate that there is not going to be either a surplus or an adequacy of PhD's in the mathematical sciences, at least for quite a few years, and consequently that many college teachers will not have the PhD degree. Many people feel that there is little more reason to suppose that the Advanced Graduate Component teachers, more than the holders of the PhD degree, will become mathematically fossilized. The general effectiveness of the mathematical teaching in colleges would be increased if demonstrably competent people without PhD degrees could be retained on faculties instead of being dismissed in order to satisfy technical requirements about the numbers of doctorate holders on faculties.

If an intermediate degree at the Advanced Graduate Component level in the mathematical sciences were to be given only by departments that already have strong PhD programs (and want to give it), the majority of our Panel on Graduate Education would be in favor of calling it a doctorate. While concurring that this level of training should receive some formal recognition, we tend to favor Professor Leonard Gillman's suggestion of the title, "Associate PhD," by analogy with Associate Professor, and with emphasis on the possibility of eventual completion of a full PhD degree.

GRADUATE-STUDENT PARTICIPATION IN UNDERGRADUATE TEACHING

There has been some criticism of the quality of mathematics teaching by graduate assistants in universities. Where this criticism is justified (and we believe that it often is not), some have adduced as a main cause the fact that teaching assistants get little or no explicit guidance as teachers. While there may be some justice in this, we feel that the major cause lies rather in an unbalanced situation, in which a fellowship or traineeship student does no teaching at all, while a teaching assistant may do so much that he cannot do it well and still carry on his own program of graduate studies. We propose changes below.

Universities use graduate assistants in freshman–sophomore mathematics teaching in two ways, mainly. Where elementary courses are taught in a number of separate sections of moderate size (20 to 30 students), graduate assistants may teach some of these sections. Where such courses are taught in large lecture sections (upwards of 100 students), graduate assistants typically conduct small recitation groups supplementing the lectures. The CBMS survey found that in academic year 1965–1966 universities with PhD programs in the mathematical sciences used large lecture sections in elementary calculus to varying degrees: approximately 55 percent of these universities used no large lecture sections at all; approximately 18 percent made some use of large lecture sections but for fewer than three fourths of their students; and approximately 27 percent used large lecture sections for three fourths or more of their students.

Our Panel on Undergraduate Education has pointed out advantages of large lecture sections, both for the students and for the graduate assistants, and has recommended that more teaching be done in this way (see the section on Methods Used to Relieve the Shortage of Teachers in Chapter 4 of reference 1). While recognizing that there are also arguments in favor of small sections and that the mathematical-science departments at many universities will not find it possible or advantageous to use large lecture sections, we believe that this recommendation deserves serious consideration.

Whatever the method a university employs for teaching its elementary courses, we firmly believe that it is important for all graduate students in the mathematical sciences to have had the experience of participating in such teaching at some time during their graduate years. Currently about 70 percent of those who obtain the PhD degree in the mathematical sciences enter academic work.* Certainly for these, some teaching experience during the graduate years (and during their early postdoctoral years as well!) is a highly practical part of career training.

We feel it is best for a graduate student in the mathematical sciences to acquire this teaching experience during his middle graduate-study years. He should not be burdened with teaching during his initial year of graduate study, when he must adjust to especially demanding and intensive course work; and during his final year of studying for his PhD degree, he may need to devote his full energies to research and thesis writing. Even during the middle graduate-study years, a graduate student's teaching load should be such that he can do justice to both his teaching and his own studies. Specifically, three to five hours a week of classroom work is as much as a graduate assistant should have to carry.

We believe that if participation in teaching is spread in this way, so that all or most graduate students do a limited amount of teaching during their middle graduate-study years, then no graduate student will have to do an excessive amount of such teaching, and the over-all quality of the teaching will improve. Arranging to spread graduate-student teaching participation in this way will plainly involve some revision in the rules and administrative procedures governing fellowships, traineeships, and teaching assistants. We believe, however, that such revision should not be overwhelmingly difficult, and that the result would be worth the effort. What seems to be needed is a larger number of fellowships and traineeships, but with a provision for limited participation in teaching during the middle graduate-study years.

* It is not correct to conclude that therefore approximately 30 percent go into industry or government. Actually, about 15 percent enter industry or government and the remaining 15 percent are simply lost track of (see reference 16). It is a fair guess that the majority of these latter come from abroad for graduate study and return to their home countries after obtaining PhD degrees, usually to enter academic work there.

9

Special Educational Issues

THE COLLEGE TEACHER

Our Panel on Undergraduate Education has given detailed consideration to a number of problems of college teachers of the mathematical sciences: see especially Chapters 4, 5, and 6 of their report.[1]

Foremost among these problems is the shortage of qualified college faculty, discussed in Chapter 4 of reference 1 and in Chapter 7 of this report. The principal way of training new qualified teachers to meet this shortage is to sustain graduate mathematical education, especially PhD production, at a vigorous level. Over the five-year period ending in 1966, PhD production in the mathematical sciences increased at an average annual rate of approximately 18 percent (see Table 10, page 139). This table also indicates that an average annual rate of only approximately 10 percent has been projected for the succeeding five-year period ending in 1971. It is also anticipated that it may not be possible to sustain the closely correlated support of basic research in the core areas at more than this level (see discussion of The Core on page 197). Much could be done to alleviate the shortage of qualified college faculty in the mathematical sciences if, for the five-year period ending in 1971, an annual rate of increase of PhD production near 18 percent instead of near 10 percent could be maintained. Also, certain measures could be taken to avoid wastage of mathematical talent at the graduate level (see the section on Wasted Mathematical Talent, page 159).

Along with the training of new faculty, however, strong and continuing efforts are needed to upgrade and update the qualifications

147

of the present college mathematical faculty. Developments in the applications of mathematics over the period 1961–1966 show sharply the changed requirements in faculty competence if students in undergraduate colleges are to be offered relevant mathematical education. The mathematical disciplines in which enrollments have grown most rapidly in this period are linear algebra, probability and statistics, and computer-related mathematics. This situation requires a substantial retraining program for the college mathematics faculty if the relevant mathematical education is to become widely available in a reasonable length of time.

The rapid growth in demand for instruction in the fields of linear algebra, probability and statistics, and computer-related mathematics from 1960–1961 to 1965–1966 is indicated in Table 11. The data are taken from the Lindquist and CBMS surveys.

TABLE 11   Growth in Certain Mathematics-Course Enrollments

FIELD	1960–1961	1965–1966	INCREASE (%)
Linear algebra	4,000	19,000	375
Probability and statistics	23,000	44,000	91
Computer-related mathematics	4,000	20,000	400
Numerical analysis	3,000	5,000	67
Analytic geometry and calculus	184,000	295,000	60
Precalculus mathematics	430,000	554,000	29
All undergraduate mathematics	746,000	1,068,000	44

During this period, mathematics-course enrollments as a whole grew at about the same rate as did undergraduate enrollments generally. College enrollment in precalculus courses grew at a much lower rate, calculus enrollment grew at a substantially higher rate, but the enrollments in linear algebra, probability and statistics, and computer-related mathematics grew at a rate spectacularly greater than did undergraduate enrollments as a whole.

In many colleges the availability of suitable courses, or even any courses, in these subjects for undergraduate students is very low, quite apart from the quality of the instruction. The CBMS survey indicates that out of the country's four-year colleges and universities there are perhaps 750 that teach mathematics to a significant number of students and yet offer no course in linear algebra. As for computing work, even more colleges offer no course in computer programming,* while only a negligible fraction offer any computer-related mathematics beyond elementary programming.

Effective action to meet this situation will have to be on a massive scale. One retrained faculty member per department will hardly be sufficient to provide the necessary nucleus if a department is to move forward to the desired level. Progress toward meeting the needs could be made with a three-year program in which, by retraining one faculty member per year, 750 mathematics departments could acquire a faculty member in each of the three areas alluded to whose retraining at least qualified him to teach strong elementary courses in this area. A new program of this breadth and magnitude would be expensive—upwards of $9 million per year, it has been estimated.

Chapter 5 of the report[1] of our Panel on Undergraduate Education eloquently points out that in the most seriously underdeveloped colleges the needs for faculty retraining are almost overwhelmingly severe and will require special measures. A number of concrete suggestions are made. We also commend to the attention of college administrations, federal agencies, and private foundations the discussion in that report (Chapters 4, 5, and 6) of other pressing problems of the college teacher: geographic and intellectual isolation from the mainstream of mathematical activities, the need for new curricula and new teaching methods, the multiplicity of demands on the college teacher's time, and the difficult working conditions and inadequate facilities with which he often has to cope.

APPLIED MATHEMATICS

The special problems of education in applied mathematics were the subject of an extensive recent conference sponsored by the Society for Industrial and Applied Mathematics. The proceedings of this conference have been published in detail,[35] and we refer to these proceedings for a full discussion, from several points of view, of some of the matters we discuss here.

It has been recognized for many years that applied mathematics does not attract a sufficient share of talent from the younger generation. Many more students could enter various fields connected with

* At least not in mathematical-science departments. In some colleges or universities where no mathematical-science department offers a course in computer programming, such a course may be available within a school of engineering or business or in some other department.

applications and pursue satisfactory and useful professional careers. Weyl's 1956 report[9] states:

The most serious problems besetting the conduct of applied mathematical training programs at present, are in order of their importance:
(1) the lack of qualified students;
(2) the difficulty of finding applied mathematicians qualified and interested to accept faculty appointments; and
(3) the questions of relative size and administrative relations of faculty organizations.

The shortage of top students in applied fields (except in computer science) is sometimes blamed on the allegedly introspective and monastic tendencies of modern mathematicians, which are said to have a pernicious effect on the teaching of mathematics. The following statement is from a letter by an applied mathematician:

Many mathematics instructors in colleges and universities proceed as if all of their students are destined to become mathematicians. They do not convey to the students the scientific origins of mathematical ideas or the possibilities of applying mathematics to natural and social sciences. They do not foster the skills necessary for future practitioners of those sciences. Instead they inculcate in the students a snobbish conviction that only pure mathematics is intellectually respectable.

This criticism may be partly justified. On the other hand, another applied mathematician wrote:

Good students are attracted by great teachers. The trouble with applied mathematics education in this country is the paucity of applied mathematicians in universities who deserve the admiration of the best students and who are able to articulate the intellectual excitement of their subject.

At any rate, we consider that the future of applied mathematics, in the broadest possible sense, depends largely on the educational efforts made today and in the near future. Two things are needed broadening of the education of young scientists and mathematician generally and education in applied mathematics as a discipline with its own objectives, attitudes, and skills. We believe that both effort should begin during the undergraduate years.

Concerning the general education, we believe that not enough is taught to students in their undergraduate work about application of mathematics, both in traditional subjects and in the very modern and new fields. There should be mathematics courses, available to all, that stress the heuristic process by which mathematical models of scientific questions are arrived at and that emphasize strongly the character of mathematical thought that leads to results from which one can infer the answers to such scientific questions. This is not the same detailed material that most efficiently leads young mathematics students to the frontiers of professional mathematics, and it requires attitudes not necessarily compatible with the attitudes of such mathematics courses. For some special students, summer sessions especially devoted to mathematics in the service of science would be a useful institution. As an example, the presentation of the range of possibilities inherent in computing machines to both undergraduate and graduate students would be timely and useful.

Such presentations would require, of course, a reservoir of professors. It would be useful to organize the preparation of a sufficient number of persons who could teach and inspire students in this direction. It also seems to us desirable to initiate, in a number of institutions, possibilities of exchange courses and lectures. What we have in mind are mathematicians teaching courses on some phases of new mathematical theories in the departments of physics, biology, or economics, and *vice versa*. Physicists and others could lecture to mathematicians on the essence of problems arising in the new developments in their own fields. In both cases, the lecturers should present the methods and the problems in the forefront of their sciences.

As far as the preparation of professional applied mathematicians is concerned, we note that this task is accomplished in various ways in various countries. In Great Britain, students enter the university either as applied mathematicians or as pure mathematicians. In the Soviet Union and in Germany, specialization takes place later in a student's career. In this country, no single system has been used, and many American applied mathematicians were originally trained as engineers or physicists. This Committee believes that one could not and should not prescribe a method for educating applied mathematicians to be used in all or most colleges and universities. On the contrary, widespread experimentation should be encouraged. Nevertheless, we want to recommend for special attention and support a plan for undergraduate education in applied mathematics which has recently been evolving at Harvard and MIT. This plan and its underlying philosophy are described in C. C. Lin's address in the proceedings[35] of the Aspen Conference, mentioned above.

Concrete educational needs in physical mathematics and other parts of applied mathematics are discussed further in Chapter 14. We emphasize, however, that unless there is a sizable core of devoted applied mathematicians who are to be judged both in professional standing and in university duties as applied mathematicians *per se*, and who are supported for their activities in applied mathematics, efforts to encourage applied mathematics are doomed to failure. Without a group of devoted, talented, and competent people, most of the crucial suggestions will not materialize. (We note, with some apprehension, that most of the specific recommendations we make concerning applied mathematics already appear in the 1956 survey.[9])

COMPUTER SCIENCE

As of the summer of 1967 there were approximately 40,000 automatic computers in the United States, excluding special military computers. In Parts I and II we have pointed out the penetration of computing into almost every facet of technical, scholarly, and economic activity. If these computers are to serve society as well as they should—indeed, if they are even to solve the complex problems society already counts on them to solve—there is a vital need for persons educated at all levels in computer science. The Pierce report[3] calls for an extremely large increase in the funds for education of college and university students in computing and for computing costs incidental to such education. Such increased activity cannot occur without a correspondingly large increase in well-educated manpower devoted to teaching computing in colleges and universities and leading the development of the subject. The total requirement for those educated in computer science certainly demands a program of massive magnitude.

These new computer scientists must be educated in our universities. The universities have heard the challenge, and departments of computer science are springing up at an ever-increasing rate. Already 50-odd departments exist at universities in the United States and Canada. In a major university not now possessing such a department there is usually a plan to create one in the near future. Although each university should certainly organize itself to best serve its own goals and constituency, it appears to us that the autonomy of a separate department offers one reasonable way to permit computer science to develop as it must. A position dominated by another science or by a branch of engineering may provide too many constraints to the development of the subject and the education of the new generation.

Once organized, departments of computer science are typically engaged in three kinds of activities:

1. Research in computer science, which may or may not involve an expensive computer laboratory;

2. Education of three classes of students: (a) future specialists in computer science at the bachelor's, master's, and/or doctor's level; (b) university students who need computing as a research tool in their university or postuniversity careers; (c) general students who wish to learn about computers as an important part of the world they live in;

3. Service to the university community. Computer scientists are typically interested in trying to help others use computing in their research, both through direct consultation and through leadership and technical advice to the university computation center.

The supply of leaders in computer science is critically low. One evidence of this is the difficulty experienced by most departments in finding suitable faculty. Another is the fact that computer science has roughly one third of the active professional workers in the mathematical sciences, yet only one twentieth of the new PhD's, and an even smaller proportion in earlier years.

What can be done about this? Clearly no ideal solution can be found for the next few years, but we see a need for a strenuous program to improve the quantity and quality of leadership as rapidly as this can be accomplished. Since it takes good faculty to produce good graduates, and good graduates to become new faculty, a classical chicken–egg problem must be solved. Since some 50-odd departments of computer science now exist, the first step would seem to be to make sure that these departments can attract as many good faculty members as can be located. With suitably high salaries and good research environments, many could be found in industry. Others can be attracted from such other university departments as mathematics and engineering, though they usually require further education in computer science.

In the better universities, at least, the new departments of computer science are finding themselves swamped by applications for admission from excellent students. (At Stanford, for example, it was possible for 1966–1967 and 1967–1968 to admit only approximately

25 students each year out of over 200 well-qualified applicants; and even so, in 1966–1967 there were more graduate students in computer science than in mathematics.) Though more reliable data are needed, it appears that in several of the best departments of computer science, the real limiting factor in the production of PhD's is not students but buildings, facilities, and faculty.

Educational programs in computer science have been the subject of several papers published in the *Communications of the Association for Computing Machinery*. See especially references 36 and 37, which give extensive details of undergraduate and graduate programs in computer science, respectively. The preliminary curricula discussed in reference 36 were planned carefully to fit in with those of the Committee on the Undergraduate Program in Mathematics. In reference 37 are given syllabi for doctoral examinations in one university, as well as a general philosophy of education in computer science.

Forsythe[37] explicitly calls attention to the need for a suitable university computation facility for use in connection with educational programs in computer science. The necessary systems include flexible, fast-acting compilers and other resident systems of a sort rarely furnished by the manufacturers of hardware. Another need is a sufficient budget for the computer time used in education; satisfactory methods of government support have not yet been worked out. Often, government accounting procedures prevent students from using university computers that are standing idle. Solving these accounting problems is important, but not easy, since they are associated with nationwide accounting policies. E. A. Feigenbaum and Courtney S. Jones have outlined the problem (see Appendix D). The problem and some proposals for its solution are also discussed in reference 38 from a different point of view.

In these early years of computer science, teaching even an elementary course is likely to be a research experience for the instructor. This implies that formal teaching loads must be lighter in computer science than in better established disciplines. This indicates need during these formative years for (a) special support for developing and updating courses in computer science, (b) support, from all sources of funds, for faculty research during the academic year, and (c) even more faculty additions than would otherwise be needed. Moreover, since much computer-science research is validated by the successful operation of computer programs rather than by the suc cessful proof of theorems, special attention has to be given to the form and character of assessment of research quality.

Because of the need to furnish computer-science students with some computing time for their work, an additional budget is needed. We make the rough estimate that graduate students in computer science each need $1,000 per year of computing time.

The most critical shortage in the computer world is for well-educated systems programmers and persons who can teach systems programming. (For example, to provide the large amount of student computing service implied by recommendations of the Pierce report,[3] without intolerable costs, will require the resourcefulness of many more systems programmers than are now available.) An essential ingredient of education in systems programming is the opportunity to experiment with the control programs of a modern computer. Such experiments cannot be tolerated on a computing machine dedicated to continuous reliable campus-wide service, because of the probability of interrupting the service. Hence, in addition to the $1,000 of computing time estimated above, advanced students specializing in systems programming will require access to a substantial computer separate from the central campus computer utility, so that systems experiments can be safely encouraged. If the experimental machine can be shared with other research projects, we estimate that the additional costs of systems experimenting may approximate $5,000 per year for the advanced student of systems programming. For comparison, we note that it is not uncommon for a student of systems programming to use $15,000 worth of computing time for thesis research.

One very important problem in computer-science education is the appropriate organization of a university in regard to computing. Because computing is such a new field, one typically finds computing groups arising in several parts of a campus—for example, in electrical engineering, in the graduate school of business, in experimental physics, in the medical school, in industrial engineering, in operations research, in the school of arts and science. Furthermore, a university may have several computation facilities. Such dispersion of effort, unless most carefully coordinated, tends to produce incompatible computer systems, duplicated faculties, and other problems. Some unpleasant campus controversies have already arisen over competition for the major role in computer-science education. We can only suggest that university administrations save money and manpower by strong coordination of efforts. The relation of the computer-science department to the university computation facility is especially important. We believe they should be sufficiently closely related to exert desirable influences on each other, and yet their distinct functions of research and education on the one hand, and university service on the other, require clearly separated administrative settings.

In today's tight fiscal situation it is extremely hard to add a burgeoning new field to an already overcrowded and overcommitted university. The new departments of computer science are typically suffering from shortages in space, in faculty, in research funds, in budget, in computer resources, and—in some cases—in research assistantships and traineeships. The problems seem to require massive infusions of new money.

STATISTICS

As has been the case for 20 years,[39] there is a wide demand for adequately trained statisticians. The diversity of the needs and of the kinds of statisticians who can help to meet them is briefly considered in the further discussion of Statistics on page 203. Most needed are statisticians who are motivated by mathematics, on the one hand, and by the challenge of dealing with uncertainty or revealing what their data are trying to say, on the other.

Unfortunately, the number of PhD's being completed in mathematical statistics in the United States today is relatively small— fewer than 10 percent of the roughly 800 PhD's per year being produced in the mathematical sciences generally, according to estimates by our Panel on Graduate Education. This is not because of too few graduate training opportunities: the country has about 70 universities that offer PhD degrees in statistics, and even those with quite strong programs are not getting many able students. Attracting more first-rate men to do PhD-level work in the field is a genuine problem.

The major difficulty lies at the undergraduate level. In statistics, as in all the mathematical sciences, preparation for research and professional activity is naturally well under way before a student completes his undergraduate years. Fewer than one half of the universities with PhD programs in statistics also offer undergraduate statistics majors. Almost no other institutions offer either such majors or majors combining statistics and mathematics. Only a small fraction of U.S. undergraduates have appreciable access to statistics as a subject. It is true that undergraduate preparation for majors in mathematics, with its traditional emphasis on core mathematics, provides an excellent foundation of knowledge for potential graduate students in statistics. It does not, however, provide nearly enough students with either motivation to study statistics or an understanding of the extramathematical aspects of statistics.

All those things that can be done at the undergraduate level to expose more students to a proper understanding of statistics and its role are urgently needed. Including mathematical statistics in a conventional mathematics major can help; the students will at least learn that there is such a subject as statistics, but they are unlikely to gain any feeling for its nonmathematical aspects. Introducing mathematics students to statistics, taught so as to communicate its extramathematical aspects, while using mathematics freely where appropriate, can help much more.

Even this does not meet the needs of the many students who might find research in statistics attractive but who happen to be repelled by the attitudes conveyed in courses of a conventional mathematics major. Majors in many fields, particularly scientific ones, have provided pathways to statistics for outstanding individuals. We cannot, however, expect these routes to meet the need. If an open road to graduate study in statistics is to be provided, the minimum is a joint program in mathematics and statistics, in which statisticians who have or can adopt an extramathematical attitude have a substantial share in setting tone and attitudes. Where faculty skills and attitudes permit and appropriate courses can be given, an undergraduate major in statistics offers greater possibilities.

The whole problem of undergraduate routes to graduate school is vital for statistics. Those departments now giving the PhD degree are already diverse in attitudes and course content, and will become increasingly so as they strive to meet the needs of an ever more heterogeneous student clientele.

Both to attract good students and to give the training they need, courses in statistics must gain excitement and realism by avoiding the impressions (all too frequent in today's courses) that: (a) the model is already available; (b) the data and the problem are small-scale and easily treated by a standard approach; (c) anything large and complex would be beyond the reach of these methods and therefore outside of statistics; (d) data are nice and clean; (e) all statistics is mathematics; (f) all statistics is based on probability (whereas much has nothing to do with it).

If this is to happen on a nationwide scale, as it should, both teachers and students will require access to new material, providing understandable accounts of enough different instances of: (a) model building; (b) large-scale investigations involving both large-scale data processing and statistical thinking; (c) "dirty" investigations skillfully handled; (d) material on the nonmathematical, nonprobability parts of statistics. As such material becomes available, there will be need for a substantial effort to make its effective use possible in many more institutions than now provide their undergraduates with effective access to statistics.

RESEARCH VERSUS TEACHING

During recent years, it has become fashionable to complain that government sponsorship of scientific research has led to poorer teaching, especially on the college level, because of separation of leading scientists from contact with undergraduates. On the other hand, many professionals believe that the teaching of the mathematical sciences in American colleges and universities is better today than it was, say, 30 years ago. In particular, the reduction in formal teaching hours that has taken place during that period has often resulted in replacing routine teaching of traditional courses by more ambitious, modern, and creative pedagogical efforts.

While it is difficult to obtain objective evidence of this, we have made an effort to ascertain whether and to what degree the leading research mathematicians are, in fact, removed from teaching in general and from undergraduate teaching in particular. At the Committee's request, the American Mathematical Society has identified about 300 distinguished American mathematicians to whom a short questionnaire concerning their teaching duties was sent. The list includes those mathematicians who have delivered invited addresses at AMS meetings or at International Congresses of Mathematicians since World War II, members of the National Academy of Sciences, and recipients of NSF Senior Postdoctoral Fellowships, Sloan Fellowships, Guggenheim Fellowships, and various other prizes.

It was found that, on the average, during the three academic years 1962–1965 all but eight of the 283 respondents taught at least three hours a week, with the typical teaching load being six hours; and all but 30 of the 283 taught some classes for or open to undergraduates. In assessing these figures, which we believe compare favorably with those in other sciences, one should remember that a research mathematician usually does more teaching in seminars and personal consultations with students than during formal instruction hours. Thus, there is considerably more teaching by such scientists than is indicated by numbers of classroom teaching hours.

WASTED MATHEMATICAL TALENT

We believe that a large number of mathematically gifted young men and women with potential to become productive mathematical scientists and college mathematics teachers fail to do so for socially determined reasons. Waste of mathematical talent occurs at two points in particular, and we feel that preventive action can be taken. The problems touched on here are clearly not peculiar to the mathematical sciences.

As noted in Chapter 7, over 70 percent of liberal arts colleges have, at most, one staff member who is a PhD in a mathematical science, and approximately 40 percent have none at all. In such institutions, talented students will in general not receive proper guidance and will almost certainly not receive undergraduate education sufficient for successful graduate careers. The situation is aggravated by the fact that in many cases students attending such institutions come from economically and culturally deprived regions and population strata.

A fuller discussion of this problem is given in Chapter 5 of the report[1] of our Panel on Undergraduate Education. This Panel has proposed various measures to improve the situation. If these measures are undertaken and are successful, they will contribute toward relieving the shortage of mathematical scientists and college teachers and will also contribute in a modest way toward the solution of an acute social problem. We endorse the recommendations of our Panel and have singled out one (Recommendation 15, page 27) that could be implemented immediately. It aims to provide a "fifth undergraduate year," which would enable exceptionally talented students with weak preparation to begin graduate work at more competitive levels of preparedness.

Our Panel on Undergraduate Education has also pointed out, in

Chapter 5 of their report,[1] that at present our society is not utilizing fully the intellectual capacity of women. Social attitudes, family responsibilities, and out-dated nepotism rules prevent many talented young women from beginning or continuing graduate study and from continuing professional work after having received a PhD degree. A modest recommendation to help alleviate the situation has been given in Recommendation 13 (page 26).

IV

Level and Forms of Support

This part of our report is devoted to description of the sources levels, and forms of support of research and higher education in the mathematical sciences by the federal government and by private foundations. There will be some discussion of industrial laboratories but no attempt will be made to assess quantitatively the contribution by industry or by the universities.

The overwhelming portion of the support considered here has its source in the federal government. The objectives of this support range widely from the immediate results sought by the supporting agency to the maintenance of lines of communication with leading mathematicians, so that potential applications of mathematics to agency problems will continue to be identified and exploited as early as possible. Although the National Science Foundation is not ordinarily thought of as a mission-oriented agency, its direct mission of supporting the advance of the main lines of scientific research as developed within the mathematical sciences is actually the most vital science mission of all.

Appropriate forms of support must accomodate themselves to a variety of objectives, to the varying relations between supply and demand of research manpower, and to the size and structure of the science activities in educational institutions.

10

Federal Support of Research

The general history of federal support of scientific research has already been clearly traced in an earlier report of the National Academy of Sciences.[41] For the mathematical sciences, the period since World War II is of special importance. During this postwar period, federal support of mathematical research and graduate education has grown significantly, stimulating and keeping pace with the general growth in American mathematical activity; and during this period the United States has moved into a position of world leadership in mathematical research (see Chapter 1).

LEVEL AND SOURCES OF SUPPORT

The principal government-wide analysis of federal research obligations is contained in the National Science Foundation series, *Federal Funds for Research, Development, and Other Scientific Activities.*[2] The figures below were obtained from Volumes IV–XV of this series. As Table 12 shows, eight agencies are currently the key federal contributors to support of research, both basic and applied, in the mathematical sciences.

At this point we make a distinction between basic and applied research. For the mathematical sciences, this is not at all the distinction between core mathematics and applied mathematical sciences. Research is basic or applied according to whether it is inner-directed or mission-oriented. Although he does not use the term "inner directed," Brooks has given a clear discussion of this idea in a

163

TABLE 12   Federal Obligations for Research in the Mathematical Sciences

| | MILLIONS OF DOLLARS | | | |
AGENCY	1960	1962	1964	1966
National Science Foundation	3.8	7.4	11.4	14.9
Army	2.7	5.5	8.3	8.6
Navy	6.9	16.3	26.2	26.5
Air Force	5.0	10.4	20.4	33.2
DOD-wide Agencies	—	6.4	14.4	19.2
Atomic Energy Commission	3.2	4.1	5.1	6.5
National Aeronautics and Space Administration	1.0	17.2	6.3	7.6
National Institutes of Health	0.1	0.1	2.6	4.3
All Others	0.9	1.6	3.3	4.1
TOTALS	23.6	69.0	98.0	124.9

recent article in *Science*.[40] Research is basic, or inner-directed, when the choices made by the researcher in the course of the research are "influenced almost entirely by the conceptual structure of the subject rather than by the ultimate utility of the results." As Brooks goes on to point out, it is perfectly consistent with this conception for the subject of a basic research to have utility and for the research to be funded with this in mind. Thus inner-directed research includes work in both core mathematics and applied mathematics. Examples of basic research in applied mathematics are studies in the mathematical theory of linguistics, dynamical systems and their astronomical applications, and the theory of rotating fluids for the understanding of geophysical phenomena.

The amounts shown in Table 12 are for the support of both basic and applied research. The over-all figures in reference 2 indicate that for 1966 the $125 million in federal obligations for mathematical-sciences research was almost equally split between basic and applied research; about $62.5 million went to basic research. According to a study made by F. J. Weyl for our Panel on Level and Forms of Support, however, certain of these figures are of uncertain reliability, so that a conservative total of $46.5 million for basic research support in 1966 seems closer to the facts. A complete tabulation of the amounts obligated by various federal agencies for support of basic research in the mathematical sciences is shown in

Table 13 along with the basic-research percentage of total research obligations.

Table 13, especially the percentage comparison with Table 12, demonstrates the striking growth of the *applied*-research effort in the mathematical sciences, based on the use that can now be made of mathematical modes of analysis together with modern computing equipment. When it comes to interpreting the dollar amounts in Table 13, it must be kept in mind that they neither coincide with nor entirely include the totals allocated for mathematical research to universities. In the budgets of the military services, about 85 percent of the amount allocated to basic mathematical research is spent in universities. In the case of the other five key agencies, less is known about any further breakdown of the reported figures.

Returning to Table 12, it had been our hope to extract in the first instance all "large" projects, say $500,000 or more in fiscal year 1966, and to specifically identify them, especially those which, although of predominantly mathematical nature, serve primarily research objectives in other disciplines. Next, we had hoped to break out of the residue the amounts allocated to in-house mathematical activity. It would have been our aim, finally, to show how the re-

TABLE 13   Basic-Research Amounts and Percentages[a]

AGENCY	1960		1962		1964		1966	
	AMT.	%	AMT.	%	AMT.	%	AMT.	%
NSF	3.8	100	7.4	100	11.4	100	14.9	100
Army	2.2	81	2.6	47	2.9	35	2.4	28
Navy	4.8	70	4.6	28	6.7	26	5.9	22
Air Force	2.0	40	3.0	29	5.4	26	6.2	19
DOD Agencies	—	—	—	0	[14.1]	[98]	[16.0]	[83]
AEC	2.8	88	3.9	95	4.9	96	6.3	97
NASA	1.0	100	[0.7]	[4]	5.4	86	7.0	92
NIH	0.1	100	0.1	100	0.8	31	2.2	51
All Others	0.3	33	0.4	25	1.2	36	1.6	40
TOTALS	17.0	72	22.0	32	38.7	40	46.5	37
			[22.7]	[33]	[52.8]	[54]	[62.5]	[50]

[a] Figures in square brackets are of uncertain reliability and therefore omitted from the unbracketed totals. The minimum in percentage of basic research shown as occurring in 1962 may be due to some artifact of the data, such as reclassification.

mainder is divided among the five major categories: core mathematics, physical mathematics, mathematical statistics, computer science, and the pioneering of mathematical methods in new areas, especially the biological and behavioral sciences. This has turned out to be impossible. In no agency does there exist a central focus for maintaining an overview regarding its entire commitment to mathematical-sciences research.

The study made for our Panel on Level and Forms of Support estimates that in fiscal year 1964 approximately $45 million were allocated by the federal government to mathematical-sciences research at universities, $16 million going to contract research centers and $29 million for academic research. The $16 million involves such organizations as Argonne National Laboratory, Lincoln Laboratory, Lawrence Radiation Laboratory, and Los Alamos Scientific Laboratory. The $29 million certainly includes almost the entire $11.4 million of the National Science Foundation. Adding also the approximately 85 percent of the $15.1 million in the Army, Navy, and Air Force budgets for basic mathematical-sciences research ($12.4 million), there is a remainder of $5 million, which must have been contributed by the AEC (perhaps about $3 million), NASA, and NIH (approximately $1 million each). Comparable amounts in fiscal year 1966 might be roughly estimated as not less than 10 percent and not more than 15 percent higher, suggesting a total current allocation to academic research in the mathematical sciences in the neighborhood of $35 million. A slightly higher growth rate—approximately 18 percent—has held in recent years for PhD production (see The Doctorate in the Mathematical Sciences, page 138) and for the closely correlated support of core research areas (see The Core, page 197).

Undoubtedly, substantial apportionments for research in the mathematical sciences are made by the key agencies, other than the AEC and the NSF (which have no in-house laboratories), to intramural research activities. In the Army alone, this accounts for about $5 million of its total $8.6 million spent for mathematical-sciences research in fiscal year 1966. Of this amount only $1 million is under the central management of the headquarters staff of the Army Research Office in the Office of the Director of Research and Development. A comparable amount is probably distributed in the laboratories of the Navy, and somewhat less in the Air Force. Once the contributions of NIH and NASA have been added to these items and combined with the mathematical research funds obligated by the remaining agencies, something like a total of $15 million may be accounted for.

THE ROLE OF THE MISSION-ORIENTED AGENCIES

The mission-oriented agencies concerned with the mathematical sciences are the agencies listed in Table 12, excluding the National Science Foundation. In this connection, two points need emphasis. First, although it is not ordinarily classed as a mission-oriented agency, the National Science Foundation itself has a very definite mission in the promotion and support of basic research and education in the sciences (see reference 41, page 46). Second, though they are not as yet extensively concerned with the mathematical sciences, mission-oriented agencies other than those listed in Table 12 will likely become so in the near future. This applies especially to agencies whose missions lie in urban development, environmental control, transportation, education, and related concerns.

A great deal of credit for the rise of the United States, during the 1950's, to a position of world pre-eminence in mathematical research is due to the vision and policies of mission-oriented agencies within the federal government, and above all those of the Department of Defense. In fact, in the critical period immediately following World War II it was a newly formed mission-oriented agency—the Office of Naval Research—that pioneered in developing contract machinery appropriate for federal support of scientific research in universities. This, together with the grant mechanisms being evolved at about the same time by the National Institutes of Health, has led to the extremely fruitful project-grant mode of federal research support (see reference 41, Chapter III). From the outset, ONR had a clear conception of the value of supporting basic research ("free rather than directed") and "maintaining contact with the most imaginative people in science" (reference 41, page 37).

A mission-oriented agency supporting research in the mathematical sciences as part of its research and development program will do so for the sake of the following major objectives:

1. The development and use of mathematical techniques, as well as the training of mathematical scientists in the fields, at the level, and in the numbers that its mission requires

Decisions of sponsorship therefore reflect an interest in particular subject-matter fields. Of course, such expectations of mission-related usefulness cannot be put on a project-by-project basis but are attached to a coherent program effort over a reasonable time. Thus, $300,000 knowledgeably invested for five to seven years in research on nonlinear ordinary differential equations will make a difference in the designing of guidance and control servos of more versatile performance. How much difference it will make, how much more difference might be made by each additional $100,000 so invested, or whether the entire amount would do better in some other area depends on such factors as the field, the people, and the problems. To raise and, no matter how imperfectly, to answer such questions is properly the concern of the research administrator.

2. Marshaling, when and as needed, the contributions that can be made to its mission by the sum total of the mathematical sciences, both as a body of accumulated knowledge and as a community of concerned and experienced scholars

Assuring the sponsor of prompt alerting and cogent advice on matters of importance to his affairs has long been recognized as an important part of research support, especially in the mathematical sciences, where the areas to be covered are generally extensive, while the manpower that can be allocated in-house is limited.

3. The contributions that the agency can make by opening up the most challenging problems that it faces for work by the research community

Manifold patterns of communication are being utilized for bringing the open scientific problems of research-sponsoring agencies before the mathematical-sciences community. Joint meetings, problem workshops, and special program activities aimed at "coupling" are all being tried, in part to get the word out and in part to create opportunities for outstanding mathematicians to influence when and as they may choose, the extension of mathematical modes of thinking in areas of science and technology currently of national concern.

We note that support of basic research by agencies with specific applied missions results in multiple sources of support, a condition that has proved beneficial for the advance of all sciences and in particular for the mathematical ones.

It is not always realized how large a fraction of federal support of the mathematical sciences in recent years has come from the mission-oriented agencies. Table 13 shows that during the period 1960 to 1966 approximately 70 percent of the federal support of basic mathematical research has been contributed by the mission-oriented agencies, that is, by the listed agencies other than the National Science Foundation. The amounts and percentages for specific years are given in Table 14.

TABLE 14   Amount and Percentage of Federal Support of Basic Mathematical Research Contributed by Mission-Oriented Agencies

	1960	1962	1964	1966
Amount (\$ millions)	13.2	14.6	27.3	31.6
Percentage	78	66	71	68

The mission-oriented agencies have always had a mandate (clarified in the President's Executive Order 10521 of March 17, 1954, as noted in reference 41, page 49) to engage in support of basic mathematical research in areas closely related to their missions; and, indeed, Table 14 indicates that this support has grown at an average annual rate of approximately 15 percent during the period 1960–1966. During the same period, however, a computation using figures from Tables 12 and 13 shows that support of *applied* mathematical research by the mission-oriented agencies has grown at an average annual rate of over 50 percent. Undoubtedly, work involving expensive computer systems accounts for a large fraction of this phenomenal growth, but this is still impressive documentation of the rapidly increasing use of the mathematical sciences by these mission-oriented agencies.

Provided it is understood that basic research in the mathematical sciences includes basic research in computer science, which involves expensive equipment, we feel that it makes sense to recommend that future support of such basic research by the mission-oriented agencies grow in proportion to these agencies' utilization of the knowledge and techniques of the mathematical sciences. We also find it appropriate that these agencies, who are themselves consumers of mathematically trained personnel and who benefit from the high level of science and technology that depends on advanced mathematical training, should continue to participate in the support of this training. Furthermore, we believe that these agencies can continue to find value in contact with first-rate academic mathematical scientists, and that, conversely, these scientists can receive valuable intellectual stimulus as well as financial support from mission-oriented agencies. In particular, the mission-oriented agencies would profit from supporting more postdoctoral research associates. Some further observations and recommendations in this general direction are made in the discussion of support by industrial and government laboratories in Chapter 13. Finally, we emphasize once more that in the future comparable recommendations may be expected to apply not only to the mission-oriented agencies of Table 12 but also to federal agencies concerned with such matters as urban development, education, environmental pollution, and natural resources.

FORMS OF SUPPORT

This Committee is aware that authoritative voices have proposed very radical changes in the whole federal system for supporting academic research and university education, abandoning the present forms of support in favor of direct federal subsidies to universities. COSRIMS felt that a discussion of this problem lay outside its competence. The fact that we do not mention this possibility in our report should not be taken as evidence that we either oppose or support it.

It is self-evident that any thorough discussion of such a radical change of the present system would have to take account of the problems of the mathematical sciences.

Currently federal support of basic mathematical-science research in institutions of higher learning, estimated above at about $35 million in fiscal 1966, assumes a variety of forms. The principal forms have been individual or group projects, conferences, departmental or block grants, and institutional grants (especially the NSF Science Development Program).

The Project System

Project support has been by far the largest single item, and the one that we consider to be most important, for research advance.

According to estimates computed for us by the CBMS Survey Committee directly from the grant lists of funding agencies, project support of basic mathematical research in universities accounted for something over $20 million in fiscal year 1966. This was primarily for "inner-directed" projects involving only occasional, and usually very minor, allowances for computers and other equipment.

Responses to the CBMS Graduate Questionnaire (reference 16, Volume II) indicate that grants of this sort provided support for the summer research activities of over 900 senior investigators (associate and full professors) and over 500 younger ones (assistant professors, instructors, and research associates), as well as academic-year support (usually only partial) for about 240 senior investigators and over 100 junior ones. In addition, they provided stipends for approximately 750 graduate research assistants, proportionately more of the graduate students in applied mathematics, computer science, and statistics being supported in this way. (Proportionately more in core mathematics are supported as teaching assistants.) Also included were small but important allowances for travel and for publication costs incidental to the projects supported.

The project system of research support is thoroughly discussed and evaluated in a 1964 report by the Committee on Science and Public Policy of the National Academy of Sciences (reference 41, Chapter VII). That report recommends (page 77) that

for the foreseeable future, the major emphasis in the federal government's support of basic research in science in institutions of higher learning should continue to be given to the project system.

We strongly endorse this recommendation. Mathematical research of high quality has resulted from the project system, especially through its use of panels of peers in assessing mathematical scientists and their research. This system has also stimulated the greatest expansion of graduate mathematical education at those institutions best qualified to give it.

A point that deserves emphasis is the relative inexpensiveness of "project support per tenure research grantee" for the mathematical sciences as compared with the physical sciences. The primary reason for this is, of course, easily understood: project grants in the mathematical sciences, even as recently as 1966, involved little in the way of computer or other equipment costs, whereas equipment costs for the physical sciences in the recent years have ranged from relatively modest, as in the case of chemistry and solid-state physics, to ex-

tremely high, as in the case of elementary-particle physics and astronomy. If for the mathematical sciences in 1966 we take the total
of project support, slightly over $20 million, and divide this by the
number of tenure researchers on project grants, approximately 920,
we obtain a little over $22,000 as the project support per tenure re-
search investigator (TRI). (It must be understood, of course, that
only a fraction of this amount actually pays for the services of the
TRI himself—typically approximately $5,000, primarily for support
of summer research activities. The rest goes for such things as support of junior researchers, research associates, and research assistants; for travel and publication costs; for clerical materials and
services; and above all—actually—for indirect costs or overhead.)

For comparison, *Physics: Survey and Outlook*,[42] pages 103 and
108, concludes that for physics in 1963 "annual research support
per active faculty investigator" could be conservatively estimated at
$60,000 and conservatively projected to 1966 at approximately
$67,000. Actually, the discrepancy between the physics and mathe-
matical-sciences figures may be much greater than this comparison
of $67,000 with $22,000 suggests, since "active faculty investigators"
in the physics computation appears to have included junior as well
as senior researchers, and perhaps even those not on grants at all.

We checked the above mathematical-sciences figure of $22,000 on
a university-by-university basis for some 15 universities. While there
was a fair spread in the results, the average was very close to this
$22,000 figure, and the spread was considerably less than when both
junior researchers and tenure researchers were taken into account.
We therefore suggest that "project support per tenure research
investigator" is a reasonably stable figure to use in projecting grant
support on a demographic basis. For the future, however, direct costs
for equipment (primarily computer costs) promise to be distinctly
higher in mathematical-science research. At the same time, indirect
costs for salaries and stipends promise to be higher too, as will be
costs for research assistants, if the recommendations below concerning numbers of research assistants are followed. As a result, we believe that for the future the $22,000 average figure will prove to be
unrealistically low and that a figure approaching $30,000 will more
nearly answer to the increased needs.*

We recognize that there have been objectionable features in the

---

* For computer science itself. the corresponding average cost is estimated to be
near $60,000 per TRI per year (see Computer Science, page 205).

operation of the project system. Its advisory panels have not always been sufficiently responsive to the newer areas of research, and the system has sometimes failed to meet effectively the needs of young investigators at less-distinguished universities and at liberal arts colleges. To help offset these disadvantages we suggest that evaluating panels should include representatives of new areas of mathematical research (in both core mathematics and applied fields), that younger investigators not at leading universities should be included in the projects of senior people at such universities, and that the projects should provide for travel funds adequate to maintain contact between the senior mathematicians and such younger men. We also have some specific new proposals to make regarding the support of young investigators (see the discussion of postdoctoral teaching fellowships in the section on Postdoctoral Research Education, page 182).

Overhead, a sizable item in project budgets, amounted in fiscal 1966 to perhaps 30 percent of gross direct costs. Recent changes in accounting procedures have, however, already begun to increase this proportion and appear certain to increase it to over 40 percent within the next few years. Actually, the effect of new cost-sharing requirements has been a shift in the allocation of the overhead burden from the experimental to the theoretical sciences, where the primary budgetary items are salaries. Unless compensating upward adjustments are made in the total funds available to these theoretical fields, the effect will be an increasingly serious net loss to research support. This effect is already beginning to be felt in the mathematical sciences.

Departmental Grants

Here we shall consider department-level grants, conceived of as a more or less indefinitely renewable mode of sustaining research activities within a department. (In the succeeding subsection we shall consider developmental grants, including grants at the department level, intended to initiate a development but not to sustain it indefinitely.)

There are advantages of simplicity and flexibility in department-level grants generally, as a supplement or partial alternative to project grants. While agreeing that departmental grants can be given only after a department has attained a minimal level of excellence, we recognize that such grants may be particularly appropriate for small departments, provided there is substantial agreement among the department faculty that this type of support is desirable, and we recommend that this type of grant be tried on an experimental basis. In order to have the desired flexibility, these departmental grants should approximate as closely as possible, in character, the relatively unrestricted grants-in-aid that have been made by private foundations. Such grants should run for about three years and should include some support of younger mathematicians, travel, graduate research assistants, and publication costs. The same principle of departmental grants should apply to developing and sustaining the efforts of strong or excellent departments if they wish to extend their activities to include new areas of research. For example, if a department of mathematics is already excellent in pure mathematics and in applied mathematics in the physical sciences, a grant in applied mathematics for the social sciences might be made available.

Developmental Block and Area Grants

Over recent years, various types of developmental block and area grants have been made. The most important federal program in this direction has been the National Science Foundation Science Development Program. Announced in the spring of 1964, this program had made 17 awards to universities by the end of fiscal 1966. Of these, 10 involved the mathematical sciences directly though not in uniform ways or to a uniform extent. Individual grants, made for three-year periods, tended to average fairly close to $4 million, but the mathematical-science percentages of these grants varied all the way from 4.3 percent to 31 percent. In total, the mathematical-science parts of these 10 grants amounted to some $4.7 million, the major portion of it awarded within fiscal 1966. In the fall of 1966, the Science Development Program was broadened to include, in addition to the original University Science Development Program, a Departmental Science Development Program at the graduate level and a College Science Improvement Program for primarily undergraduate institutions.

Our Panel on New Centers has made a special study and evaluation of the NSF university development grants affecting the mathematical sciences. Queries by the Panel to recipient institutions confirm that the major use to which the mathematical portions of these grants have been put, or are planned to be put, is the procurement of high-quality research faculty. Other uses of the grants include library improvement, computer installations, fellowships, salary increases, and the provision or improvement of administrative and clerical services.

Among recipients of the university development grants there are institutions in which a serious effort in coordinating the development of the mathematical sciences with that of other scientific disciplines has been successfully fostered by the grant. Indeed, we feel that such mathematical sciences as computer science and statistics are by their very nature especially well adapted to interdisciplinary grants. On the other hand, in the cases of two institutions, the awarding of strongly interdisciplinary grants led to considerable friction between the mathematics department and the other departments involved, and the outcome was on the whole detrimental to the development of mathematics in these institutions. For this reason especially, we welcome the broadening of the NSF Science Development Program to include a departmental program and feel that the added flexibility thus introduced will prove particularly valuable to departments of mathematics.

Concurring with our Panel on New Centers, we do not wish to take a stand relative to geographical considerations in the establishment or development of new centers. We feel that geographical considerations transcend the mathematical sciences as such and are concerned with more general questions of policy that will not be resolved by any simple formula. We do, however, wish to identify and comment on three types of possibilities relating to geographical considerations.

One of these possibilities is the development of new centers in close proximity to existing major centers. Assuming the proper departmental and administrative conditions for the development of an important new center, a university near one or more existing major centers should find the recruitment of the proper type of new faculty relatively easy. This is particularly true of junior faculty members who want to be in frequent contact with important contributors to research and who want to be able to attend seminars and colloquia at the nearby major centers. The payoff in positive influence in the geographical area of the new center is correspondingly less, however, since the area already has top-level mathematical activity.

Second, there is the possibility of developing new centers in large metropolitan areas without existing major centers. It seems self-evident that the longer-range scientific effort of the country will be enhanced by the deliberate development of important scientific and mathematical centers in those larger metropolitan areas that have not developed their own major educational centers. Here, assuming the proper departmental and administrative conditions, it should be possible in a somewhat longer period of time to develop important new mathematical centers that, in turn, should tend to improve the education and scientific activity in the given metropolitan area. The payoff should be greater but the task harder than in areas close to existing centers.

A third possibility is the creation of new centers in educationally underdeveloped larger geographical areas. The problem of creating major new centers in such areas is greatly complicated by the general educational level and the apparent relative unattractiveness of such areas for top-level younger mathematicians. Such considerations extend not only to schools for the children of mathematicians but to the university and graduate-level recruitment of talented students. Whereas the difficulties of major improvement are the greatest, the payoff for success is the greatest in important side effects on the whole educational process in a large area. It seems likely that support for the development of several nearby centers in a given geographical area may be an effective way to accelerate the desired growth process and make recruiting of talented younger mathematicians easier. Advantage should be taken of improved socio-economic conditions when these are present.

The NSF Science Development Program has sometimes been described as aimed at creating "new centers of excellence." As far as departments of mathematics are concerned, this program has in practice aimed mainly at raising them to the "strong" level, rather than the "distinguished" one, in the rating of Cartter's study,[32] page 66. The nine departments classified by Cartter as distinguished are responsible for the education of a disproportionately large number of American research mathematicians (see Appendix E, Table E-3), and it is certainly in the national interest to increase the number of such departments. We caution, however, against the idea that money in itself is sufficient to create such new centers of excellence. There are two striking examples of universally recognized, excellent departments of mathematics that could not have been created except for massive infusion of federal funds. These are the Mathematics Department at Stanford University and the Courant Institute at New York University. In both cases, however, there were unusual circumstances; a strong nucleus of first-rate mathematicians was already attached to these institutions at the very beginning of their activities. It does not seem likely that similar opportunities, which in these instances resulted from political conditions in Europe in the 1930's, will be repeated in the near future.

TIME AND EFFORT REPORTING*

Prominent members of the mathematics community have expressed strong concern to us and to the Division of Mathematical Sciences of the National Research Council about the unreasonableness and the dangers of recent requirements of faculty "time and effort reporting" in connection with university cost-sharing on project grants. We realize that this is a matter affecting the entire scientific community and not just mathematicians; however, research in the mathematical sciences differs, in its independence of place and tools, from research in other sciences. We feel that a statement from us may be useful both to federal agencies and to university administrations.

If a university is to share salary costs as its required contribution to a project, it certainly has an obligation to provide evidence that it has actually contributed its share. It must, however, take care that it does this in a way that does not corrode the traditional relationship between the professor and the university.

Mathematical research (in common with research in such fields as theoretical physics) is not tied to a laboratory, a library, or an office. A mathematical scientist, once immersed in a problem, finds himself thinking about it at all sorts of odd moments; the duration and intensity of his research work cannot be measured quantitatively. Neither he nor, indeed, any professor can distinguish precisely between the research and educational aspects of, for example, a conference with a graduate student. Consequently, a report in

---

* Since this section was written, the Bureau of the Budget has, in response to the opposition of virtually all universities and many federal administrators as well, dropped most of its time and effort reporting requirements for university professorial staff [see "Effort Reporting: Government Drops Much-Criticized Paperwork," *Science, 160,* 1322 (June 21, 1968)]. We feel, however, that the present clear statement of the mathematical community's position on the matter may still be of value, as a cautionary reminder of the issues of integrity and university–professor relations involved.

definite quantitative terms of a scientist's allocation of his time to various activities over a short period (a month or a quarter) is impossible to give honestly and meaningfully; this impossibility is particularly acute for a mathematical scientist. To impose a requirement that is impossible of honest fulfillment is to undermine the traditional and essential relation of mutual trust and good faith between the scientist and his university.

An acceptable arrangement must recognize that in many universities a professor's salary is not paid exclusively for his teaching but in large part for his research on problems of his own choosing. Furthermore, no sharp line can be drawn between the part of this research that is performed with outside support and the part that is performed as part of the professor's general obligation to the university.

We therefore urge that federal fiscal offices and university business officers work with the academic research community to develop accounting requirements, appropriate to each individual university and discipline, that will provide proper information in a way that will preserve the integrity of the scientific community. We also note the following resolution passed by the Council of the American Mathematical Society meeting in Toronto on August 29, 1967:

The Council of the American Mathematical Society urges responsible university officers to take immediate action to have Time and Effort Reports and similar documents pertaining to faculty members' time eliminated, because it considers that such documents are incompatible with academic life and work. The Council reiterates the traditional view that teaching and research are inseparable, and that accounting procedures in universities must take account of their unitary character.

11

Federal Support of Education

In this chapter we survey federal support of higher education in the mathematical sciences, considering separately graduate education, postdoctoral research education, and the continuing education of college teachers. Under this last heading we also note briefly the National Science Foundation's support of certain other activities designed to improve undergraduate education, notably the valuable studies and conferences of the CUPM. As observed in the introductory paragraphs of Part III, our report does not concern itself directly with the extensive activities in support of curriculum revision and continuing teacher training for the elementary and secondary school levels.

GRADUATE EDUCATION

Where graduate students are concerned, federal support of research merges directly into support of education. In fact, one form of graduate-student support, research assistantships, has already been noted above in our discussion of project grants. More important, the intellectual activities central to research and advanced graduate education are literally inseparable, a point that has also been emphasized in the preceding chapter.

The CBMS survey found that in academic year 1965–1966 some 750 research assistants were supported on project grants in the mathematical sciences. We observe that, since some 900 senior mathematical scientists (associate and full professors) were on federal research grants for the summer of 1966, this gives an average ratio of less than one research assistant to each senior research grantee. We feel that the research assistantship is a valuable form of graduate-student support, especially because of the local control and flexibility in the appointment of research assistants. As a goal for the immediate future, an average ratio of one research assistant to each senior research grantee would seem reasonable, with the ratio continuing to be highest in such mathematical sciences as computer science and statistics, as is the case now.

Apart from research assistantships, federal support of graduate students assumes two principal forms: fellowships and traineeships. With the exception of fellowships awarded under the National Defense Education Act (NDEA), fellowships are awarded by the granting agencies directly to students. Traineeships and NDEA fellowships are awarded in blocks to institutions, which in turn award them to students. For fiscal 1966 the CBMS survey found that some 1,200 graduate students in the mathematical sciences were supported on federal fellowships and some 630 on federal traineeships. The total magnitude of this support was slightly over $10 million, as shown in Table 15.

TABLE 15   Federal Fellowships and Traineeships in the Mathematical Sciences for Fiscal Year 1966

FORM OF SUPPORT	$ MILLIONS
NSF predoctoral fellowships	3.1
NDEA graduate fellowships	3.1
Other federal fellowships	0.2
NSF traineeships	2.0
Other federal traineeships	1.6
NSF summer fellowships for teaching assistants	0.2
TOTAL	10.2

Altogether, federal fellowships, traineeships, and research assistantships supported about 28 percent of the approximately 9,400 full-time mathematical-science graduate students in U.S. universities in academic year 1965–1966, as Table 16 shows in more detail.

As noted in the preceding section, we feel that it is federal support of graduate students together with federal project-grant sup-

TABLE 16   Sources of Support of Graduate Students in the Mathematical Sciences in Academic Year 1965–1966

SOURCE OF SUPPORT	NUMBER SUPPORTED	PERCENTAGE SUPPORTED
Federal fellowships	1,203	13
Federal traineeships	632	7
Federal research assistantships	754	8
Private fellowships	366	4
Teaching assistantships	3,625	38
Self-supporting	2,782	30
TOTALS	9,362	100

port that has been decisive in the rise of the United States to a position of world pre-eminence in the mathematical sciences, and that these forms of support will be decisive for the maintenance of this U.S. position in the future. Furthermore, in the face of the intensified shortage of qualified college teachers of the mathematical sciences discussed in Chapter 7, we are especially concerned that federal fellowship and traineeship programs at least keep pace with, and support, the projected 10 percent per year growth in mathematical-science PhD production. Thus we would recommend that federal fellowships and traineeships combined continue to support, as Table 16 shows they did in academic year 1965–1966, about 20 percent of the expanding full-time graduate-student population in the mathematical sciences (see Chapter 2, Recommendation 11).

In accordance with recommendations of our Panel on Undergraduate Education, we also propose two special-purpose programs for support of graduate students in the mathematical sciences. Their aim is to broaden and improve opportunities for graduate study by women and by graduates of weaker or less well-known colleges.

The first of these programs, for women, is designed to offset to some degree the dropout rate of women between receipt of the BA and PhD degrees, a rate which postwar figures suggest is perhaps six times as high as the rate for men. The program recognizes that a woman's graduate study may have to be part time or may have to involve retraining after several years' absence. The specific recommendation to federal funding agencies is for 100 special part-time graduate fellowships for women. Accompanying this is a recommendation to academic institutions to provide more opportunities for part-time employment of women and in particular to remove nepotism rules that prohibit or restrict teaching in the same institution by husband and wife.

The second of these programs, for graduates of weaker or less well-known colleges, is designed to afford such students the opportunity to prove themselves in their early graduate years and to encourage them, if successful, to enter college teaching. The program recognizes that such students represent a "higher risk" and that they may require extra preparatory courses prior to full graduate work. The proposal calls for tuition scholarships, perhaps 200 a year, supplemented by "forgivable loans" to cover the initial years in graduate school, with a portion of the loan, perhaps 20 percent, to be forgiven for each year the student subsequently spends in college teaching.

More details concerning these two special proposals and the problems they are designed to meet are given in the Report of our Panel on Undergraduate Education,[1] Chapters 1 and 5.

POSTDOCTORAL RESEARCH EDUCATION

A limited number of research mathematical scientists are supported under various federal postdoctoral fellowship programs. The CBMS survey found that during academic year 1965–1966 approximately 100 U.S. mathematical scientists were in residence at U.S. universities under postdoctoral fellowships and research instructorships. About one third of these were holding awards under the National Science Foundation's regular and senior postdoctoral fellowship programs. Such awards have remained fairly steady in number over recent years, as Table 17 shows.*

We feel that, especially for the young research investigator, more such support is needed. In all sciences, and certainly in the mathematical ones, the immediate postdoctoral years are crucial for firmly launching young PhD's on research careers. At the same

---

* *Added in proof:* Owing to lack of funds, the National Science Foundation has entirely suspended for academic year 1968–1969 its program of senior postdoctoral fellowships. See *Fellowships and Research Opportunities in the Mathematical Sciences,* Division of Mathematical Sciences, National Research Council, September 1968, p. 3.

TABLE 17   National Science Foundation Regular and Senior Postdoctoral Fellowships in the Mathematical Sciences

FISCAL YEAR	REGULAR POSTDOCTORALS	SENIOR POSTDOCTORALS
1962	17	5
1963	29	5
1964	26	7
1965	21	8
1966	27	7

time many feel that capable young PhD's at academic institutions should be doing some teaching as well as research during these years and should be encouraged to seek teaching positions in a broader range of colleges and universities.

Research instructorships and postdoctoral fellowships are presently available for no more than 100 young mathematicians each year; but we feel that by 1969, which is as early as new programs could be implemented, such opportunities could profitably be offered to 200 or 300. This would be about 20 to 30 percent of the 1,000 PhD degrees that we may reasonably anticipate will be awarded in the mathematical sciences in 1969. (Young's PhD study in the CBMS Survey Report[16] suggests that in recent years only approximately 15 percent of the PhD's in the mathematical sciences have become consistently productive research mathematicians; it is this percentage that we believe can be improved.) For this situation we would like to recommend to federal funding agencies two new programs of teaching fellowships for the immediate postdoctoral years.

The first proposal, coming from our Panel on Undergraduate Education, calls for approximately 50 two-year teaching fellowship awards for young PhD's who would carry out research activities at a major mathematical center while teaching a course or two at a nearby smaller college. The purpose is the dual one of helping to launch young PhD's on academic careers of research and teaching while encouraging the distribution of such research and teaching talent to a broader range of colleges.

Another proposal deserving serious study would offer two-year teaching fellowships for postdoctoral training at regional centers located at well-established mathematical centers around the country. Beyond the objective of further training in research and acquisition of teaching experience, there would be the hope that, after two years of working together, small groups of these trained PhD's might be willing to go together to form research nuclei in a university or in a geographical cluster of smaller colleges.

Continuing Education for College Teachers

The report[1] of our Panel on Undergraduate Education and Chapter 9 of the present report have emphasized the importance of keeping college teachers of the mathematical sciences professionally alive and knowledgeable about new developments.

The principal academic-year program with this objective is the National Science Foundation Science Faculty Fellowship Program. Table 18 shows the numbers of mathematical awards under this program in recent years.

TABLE 18   National Science Foundation Science Faculty Fellowships in the Mathematical Sciences

FISCAL YEAR	POSTDOCTORAL FELLOWSHIPS	PREDOCTORAL FELLOWSHIPS
1962	18	49
1963	19	57
1964	23	59
1965	16	60
1966	16	72

The Science Faculty Fellowship Program offers an excellent way to upgrade and update college and university faculty in the mathematical sciences. In view of the continuing and seriously growing need for such upgrading and updating, this NSF program merits very considerable expansion. As a minimal objective, the Science Faculty Fellowship Program should be expanded gradually to provide for about 150 awards in the mathematical sciences by 1971, roughly double the number in recent years. Fiscally this would amount to an expansion from $1 million to perhaps $2.5 million by 1971. Our Panel on Undergraduate Education has estimated that a program of this expanded size would offer opportunity for awards to approximately one quarter of the doctorate faculty and one half of the non-doctorate faculty at least once in their teaching careers.

Only a very limited number of the more than 10,000 college teachers of the mathematical sciences can be on leave in any given academic year to take advantage of fellowship programs. The most favorable time for training activities for larger numbers of college teachers is during the summer. The NSF already sponsors limited programs of such summer activities for college teachers in the form of summer institutes, research-participation projects, and short courses, conferences, and seminars. For college mathematical-science teachers in the summer of 1966 the total magnitude of these programs was approximately $1.4 million, the major item being summer institutes of various sorts.

The Mathematical Association of America has urged a greatly expanded program in this direction in a resolution addressed to the Congress of the United States and the officers of the NSF.[4] In addition, the Association's Committee on Institutes and the Panel on College Teacher Preparation of CUPM have issued a joint report on summer institutes[5] which says, in part, ". . . a greatly expanded effort in the direction of summer institutes of all types is urgently needed . . . Even if summer institutes are to reach only 10 percent of all college mathematics teachers each summer, the number of institutes will need to be approximately tripled."

The NSF also supports, at a modest level, certain other activities designed to improve undergraduate education in the mathematical sciences. Support of these activities—encompassing course content improvement programs, curriculum conferences, acceleration of student development, instructional equipment, and visiting scientists—amounted in 1966 to approximately $2.7 million. An especially important item here has been support of the Committee on the Undergraduate Program in Mathematics. The published curriculum studies and recommendations of CUPM have formed valuable guidelines for college curriculum development in the mathematical sciences; these have, in fact, been used extensively by our Panel on Undergraduate Education in writing its report. We feel that continued support of CUPM, as well as of the college visiting lecturer program and these other NSF-funded activities, is justified, and we heartily endorse the resolution of the Mathematical Association of America to this effect.[4]

In concluding this section we invite attention to the report[1] of our Panel on Undergraduate Eduction, and particularly Chapters 5 and 6 of that report, in which the special problems and needs of the undergraduate teacher of the mathematical sciences are discussed in detail.

12

Private Foundations

Private foundations play a special role in the support of research and teaching in the sciences. It is generally their aim to seek out innovative activities and modes of support rather than to contribute toward the kinds of support already being provided by federal or other agencies.

Where the mathematical sciences have participated in the grants of private foundations it has usually been as a feature of projects to strengthen research and teaching in the sciences generally or to enhance the scientific capabilities of some institution. Also, in grants made by private foundations for other purposes, the mathematical sciences have appeared as tools, as, for instance, in the construction of mathematical models as one of the activities supported under grants in economics. It is thus difficult to separate out the mathematical-science portion of support by private foundations, and any attempt to do so must be somewhat arbitrary.

Here attention is focused on grants or portions of grants by private foundations made to aid or encourage work "by mathematicians in a mathematical setting," including work in both pure and applied mathematics but attempting to exclude mathematical activities incidental to projects in other fields.

GRANTS BY PRIVATE FOUNDATIONS

Over the period 1955–1966 the seven private foundations most heavily concerned made grants in the mathematical sciences total-

187

TABLE 19   Grant Support of the Mathematical Sciences by Private Foundations from 1955 through 1966

FOUNDATION	TOTAL 1955–1966 ($ MILLIONS)
Carnegie Corporation of New York	3.2
Ford Foundation	3.3
John Simon Guggenheim Foundation	0.4
Louis W. and Maud Hill Family Foundation	0.6
Research Corporation	0.2
Rockefeller Foundation	1.1
Alfred P. Sloan Foundation	10.4
	19.2

ing some $19.2 million, as shown in Table 19. This would indicate that the total annual contribution of grants by private foundations toward research and higher education in the mathematical sciences has averaged somewhat under $2 million in recent years.

The purposes for which these grants were made have included the formation of new mathematical centers (including the construction of buildings), strengthening of existing departments, research fellowships, special research support for younger mathematicians, strengthening of ties between pure and applied mathematics, stimulation of the use of computers, establishment of regional centers of learning, and a variety of other activities to improve curricula and teaching in the mathematical sciences. More details are given in Appendix C.

COMMENTS

We applaud the unique pioneering efforts of the private foundations in support of research and education in the mathematical sciences and feel that these foundations can hardly do better than to continue to seek out for support new activities and those that deserve more support than they are receiving from other sources.

Specific kinds of projects that our panels have commended to the attention of private foundations for possible support include the following: selected new programs for the continuing education of college faculty; new and experimental systems of publication and communication; new graduate-level curriculum studies by the Committee on the Undergraduate Program in Mathematics; studies evaluating present programs of degrees intermediate between the MA and the PhD, and gauging their acceptance by academic administrators and accrediting agencies; physical facilities (such as needed office space or departmental libraries or common rooms) not otherwise available; programs for graduate education or retraining directed toward the special problems and needs of women mathematicians; experimental regional centers for curriculum and course development; special studies of the problems of the underdeveloped colleges.

13

Industrial and Government Laboratories

A significant number of industrial and government laboratories support research and educational activity in the mathematical sciences. Accurate and comprehensive data on the extent and character of this support are, however, almost completely lacking. In order to garner preliminary information on the basis of which a rough assessment could be made and more systematic surveys might be undertaken in the future, COSRIMS and the CBMS Survey Committee jointly sponsored a Panel on the Mathematical Sciences in Industry and Government.

This Panel invited statements regarding their mathematical research and educational activities from a sample of industrial and government laboratories where such activities were known informally to be substantial. Those from which responses were received included the following:

Argonne National Laboratory
Bell Telephone Laboratories
Bettis Atomic Power Laboratory (Westinghouse Corporation)
Boeing Scientific Research Laboratories
David Taylor Model Basin
International Business Machines Corporation
Lockheed Palo Alto Research Laboratory
Los Alamos Scientific Laboratory
MITRE Corporation
Mobil Oil Corporation
National Bureau of Standards

190

Pacific Northwest Laboratory (Battelle Memorial Institute)
RAND Corporation
Sandia Corporation Laboratory

The strength and variety of mathematical activities exhibited in the responses of these selected laboratories is no doubt considerably greater than in industrial and government laboratories generally.

ACTIVITIES AT SOME MAJOR LABORATORIES

Activities at the above-listed laboratories in support of mathematical research and higher education are quite varied and in some instances surprisingly extensive. Industrial laboratories have sometimes made developmental grants in the sciences to institutions of higher education and, occasionally, grants-in-aid directly to departments of mathematics. They have also on occasion endowed distinguished chairs of mathematics in universities. Activities of these kinds are certainly valuable and deserve to be applauded and encouraged. The main contribution of industrial and government laboratories to the mathematical sciences lies, however, in their own in-house research and education efforts, and in the interplay of these with work in universities. The proportion of PhD's to total staff in the mathematical sciences at such laboratories is generally much lower than in a university. Naturally an attempt is made to appoint PhD's whose research interests will fit in with those of the laboratory, but, once appointed, such a PhD will normally be given very considerable freedom in his research activities. Direct consulting on company problems typically plays a relatively minor role, and self-initiated basic research may play a very considerable one. In this way there is direct support of mathematical research on the part of industrial and government laboratories, and top mathematicians from these laboratories are among frequent contributors of mathematical research articles and monographs.

At their best, the physical facilities and general conditions of work in these laboratories can be quite attractive. Technical libraries and library services tend to be good, and there are usually active in-house seminars and colloquia in various branches of the mathematical sciences. Provision is frequently made for bringing in distinguished university mathematicians as consultants and research collaborators, for periods varying from a day or two to several weeks or a full summer or year. In the other direction, the laboratory may give a year's leave of absence to a distinguished mathematician on its staff when he is invited to serve as a visiting professor at a university. In such a case, the laboratory may supplement his university salary. The laboratory may also provide released time to its mathematical scientists for teaching individual graduate courses at nearby universities.

Several industrial and government laboratories have attractive fellowship programs under which selected employees may study part time for PhD degrees in the mathematical sciences at neighboring universities. These programs will often provide for a year's leave of absence, at three-fourths to full pay, to work on a dissertation. The over-all magnitude of such programs is modest but not negligible. Thus the CBMS survey found that, for academic year 1965–1966, out of some 1,570 federal and private fellowships for full-time graduate study in the mathematical sciences, approximately 55 were sponsored by industry, through not all of these were fellowships for employees.

There are also laboratory-supported programs of graduate mathematical education for employees at somewhat lower levels. In one strongly research-oriented industrial laboratory it is standard practice for incoming bachelors in engineering and in mathematics to take, as part of their work for the company, a two- to three-year half-time educational program. Some of the courses are taught in extension programs at the laboratory itself, but part of the work is conducted at nearby universities and normally leads to a master's degree. The program for engineering bachelors is heavily weighted in the direction of mathematics, while the program for mathematics bachelors generally includes intensive work with computers.

THE GENERAL SITUATION AND ITS PROBLEMS

The above paragraphs have depicted qualitatively, at their present best, an enlightened attitude toward mathematical-research activities among a few major industrial and government laboratories and a healthy interaction between these activities and those of the mathematical-science departments of universities. It would be quite misleading, however, not to emphasize that this enlightened attitude and healthy interaction appear to be far from the norm.

Many applied mathematicians feel that industrial and government laboratories have generally failed to use mathematicians effectively and, what is worse, are unable to imagine or evaluate the mathematician's contribution. Informal interviews with numerous mathematicians in technologically sophisticated industries suggest that the majority of these mathematicians are in a kind of limbo in their companies. Some industrial mathematicians are vigorous in asserting that management does not use, or know how to use, their services. Too many industrial mathematicians are regarded as "mathematical repairmen," people kept around to "fix mathematics that is breaking down" but in activities of a rather routine nature.

Partly, the problem is one of communicating effectively, so that the mathematical talent within an industrial organization can be brought to bear on its mathematical problems. Many "applied mathematics sections" in industry have failed because this problem was not solved. On the other hand, when a company tries to "sprinkle" its mathematicians throughout the organization, communication lines tend to be very localized, and each mathematician is unrealistically expected to be a jack of all trades. Continued failure to solve such extremely difficult problems threatens to impede the effective use of mathematicians in industry for years to come.

There is also a problem of lack of communication and cooperation between the academic world and industrial and government laboratories. Quite a few industrial and applied mathematicians feel that the academic world is content with this situation, and that by and large universities are making little effort to prepare mathematicians for positions outside universities. This is a principal reason for our recommendation below for increased exchanges between laboratories and universities.

COMMENTS

We feel that more young mathematicians could be profitably drawn toward the work of industrial and government laboratories; thus we recommend that a special effort be made to increase the opportunities for postdoctoral research appointments in such laboratories. Specifically, a group of cooperating industries might undertake to support postdoctorals and to evaluate applications for postdoctoral appointments to industrial laboratories on a national basis through a committee of the National Research Council. At the same time we recommend an increased reverse flow of more senior mathematicians from industrial and government laboratories to universities on a temporary basis; we feel that such laboratories should be encouraged to send personnel to universities for a year or two after several years of work in the laboratory. In this connection, we call attention to the desirability of extending more senior postdoctoral opportunities to industrial personnel. The advantages of using more industrial personnel in graduate teaching and research direction should also be recognized. This should be encouraged, either as a form of industrial support of the universities or as a program supported by a combination of government and university resources.

We point out the desirability of studies leading to more accurate and comprehensive information on work in the mathematical sciences in industry and government, including present and projected manpower estimates at various levels of mathematical training. The qualitative picture drawn in the discussion of Activities at Some Major Laboratories (page 191) has emerged from case studies of a few of the country's major industrial and government laboratories. A more comprehensive study should include all these laboratories and the changing picture of mathematical work in industry and government generally. In particular, it should take account of the smaller mathematical consulting firms now springing up, firms that contract with a variety of industrial and commercial customers to do computer programming and systems analyses and mathematical operations-and-management studies.

V

Conclusions

The intellectual content and the present state of the mathematical sciences have been described in Part II. In Part III we have considered the educational problems of these sciences, and in Part IV we have discussed the present status and trends of financial support. In Part V we first discuss the tasks and needs of the mathematical sciences, primarily as far as research support is concerned. The final Chapter places these tasks and needs in the context of the mathematical sciences' total service to society.

14

Tasks and Needs

It is inevitable that in considering the tasks and the needs of the mathematical sciences we treat the various disciplines separately. We hope that this way of presentation will not obscure the intellectual ties between the mathematical sciences. To preserve these ties is itself an essential need of the mathematical community.

Over and above the specific needs enumerated below, there is a general need of the mathematical sciences, and of sciences in general, for an atmosphere in which they can flourish. This involves not only the availability of financial support but also a broad understanding of and appreciation for intellectual endeavor, a willingness to support theoretical work, and an uncompromising commitment to intellectual freedom.

THE CORE

Research within the core is primarily concerned with identifying, extending, and refining the critical concepts that serve to organize mathematical thought and with the precise analysis of the interrelations of these concepts. It is often the concepts and theorems of the core areas that breathe life into the applications of mathematics. Support for research in the core subjects thus represents capital investment in mathematics.

As an illustration, we mention that electrical engineers, computer scientists, and others are now demanding that the undergraduate curriculum in mathematics should include a sizable amount of so-called discrete mathematics. This includes such topics as the theory of algorithms, lattice theory, graph theory, and other parts of combinatorial mathematics. All these topics grew up in or around algebra at a time when it seemed that, for the most part, only "continuous mathematics," that is, mathematical analysis, was of concern to applications.

Up to now, most mathematical ideas and techniques have been developed within the core, though often as a response to challenging problems coming from outside mathematics. There is every reason to believe that the process will continue. The central core of mathematics is also the laboratory in which progress in mathematical sciences is ultimately unified and integrated. Finally, it provides an unequaled training ground for mathematicians in all fields. Many leaders in the new applied areas of mathematical sciences received their training in the rigorous atmosphere of established pure mathematics. Many future leaders in these fields, as well as leaders in fields not yet initiated, may also develop in this way.

It is our opinion that maintaining the health and vigor of research in core mathematics is essential for the health of all the mathematical sciences and, indeed, for our scientific life as a whole. It would be tragic if a misdirected drive for immediate applicability or a dominant criterion of social usefulness should be permitted to destroy or weaken the position of unchallenged leadership in mathematics now occupied by this country.

It is useful to examine how much support has been directed to the core areas of mathematics and how effective it has been. Classifying research by subject matter presents far less of a problem than classification as pure or applied. Still, boundaries between subjects are not sharp, and it is not always possible to identify the subject of a research project by looking at its title. Probability theory, for example, presents a particular problem, because a great deal of the support for research in probability has been administered in connection with statistics.

Altogether the federal government seems to have spent approximately $15 million on core-area research in fiscal year 1966. With some reservations concerning the accuracy of our classification, it appears that the Mathematical Sciences Section of the National Science Foundation (NSF) obligated about $8 million to the support of core research in fiscal year 1966 out of a total obligation of $14.9 million. The three Department of Defense (DOD) research offices—the Army Research Office, the Office of Naval Research, and the Air Force Office of Scientific Research—have each devoted about 40 percent of their mathematical research budgets to core subjects. For fiscal year 1966 this came to $5.8 million for core research. Although a much larger sum ($124.9 million) was reported as obligated in fiscal year 1966 by various federal agencies to research in the mathematical sciences, very little appears to have been spent on core research except through NSF and the three DOD offices. The National Aeronautics and Space Administration, for example, spent $91,000 on core research out of a total of more than $7 million for mathematical research. No doubt the largest unaccounted federal contribution to the core areas came through the research done by full-time employees of the government and of private research institutes such as RAND and the Institute for Defense Analyses, which are largely supported by the government.

There can be no doubt that American mathematics has moved into a position of world leadership during the period in which federal support of science has grown. But it would be difficult to decide to what extent this is due to research support. We can, however, inquire whether the money does or does not go for the support of those mathematicians who are actually producing the research that justifies the country's claim to leadership. A check of three leading American mathematical-research journals (*American Journal of Mathematics, Annals of Mathematics,* and *Journal of Mathematics and Mechanics*) for 1966 shows that 133 of the 221 papers (about 60 percent) published carry a footnote acknowledging federal support of the research reported. A similar count in a journal devoted to short papers (*Proceedings of the American Mathematical Society*) showed that 49 of 113 papers (about 40 percent) in two issues acknowledged federal support. These figures show that federal money has been involved in a truly significant portion of the mathematical research being done in this country.

It appears that the support has been effective, since great progress has been made toward the goals that might reasonably have been set 10 or 15 years ago. There has been astonishing progress within the discipline itself; a number of long-standing problems have been solved that a dozen years ago seemed almost unapproachable. Moreover, this activity in the core seems to have had the desired indirect effects. Techniques and concepts invented to solve core problems are finding applications in other areas, interest in mathematics has increased, and the number of mathematicians has grown significantly. While some local dissatisfactions exist, as they inevitably must, there is every reason to be pleased with support policies as they have affected the core areas until now.

Although there has been a generally satisfactory pattern of support in the past, the signs for the future are disquieting. The gross budget for mathematical sciences in the four agencies that support core mathematics was fixed for fiscal year 1967 at about the same size as that for fiscal year 1966. Coupled with the new rules, which allow a larger proportion of direct costs to be charged as overhead, a net decrease in funds for core research in mathematics is to be expected at a time when both the per capita cost of research and the number of qualified investigators have increased.

If funding does not show an increase commensurate with the net growth of the nation's mathematical activity, we must expect that the forces that have linked the expansion of core research to the general expansion of mathematical competence will work in reverse. Needless to say, at a time when the demand for mathematically trained personnel is expanding in every facet of our society, such a reversal would be regrettable. We may be simply unable to meet our needs in the areas of general science, education, technology, technical management, and defense.

In an area in which the effects of support on major national goals are only indirect, it is extremely difficult to judge the optimum levels of support. The core areas in the mathematical sciences have been making very good progress in recent years on support, which has been increasing at about 18 percent per annum. No one can say that this rate is necessary to achieve our goals, but it would seem imprudent to allow the growth to fall significantly below this level at a time when, according to all estimates, further expansion is necessary.

A specific need of core mathematics is the preservation of the established great centers. Their importance should not be obscured by the recognized need to develop new centers of research and education. A great center of mathematics requires a certain critical number, never precisely determined, of first-rate mathematicians. It must attract some of the best students. At such a place there is a spirit of high tension, an awareness of the important problems, and a willingness to explore new approaches and to accept new ideas, coupled with a sense of history and uncompromisingly high standards.*

---

* A famous example of a great mathematical center was the University of Göttingen in Germany. Göttingen was the world capital of mathematics until 1933. Its fame dates from the times of Gauss and Riemann, but it became a great school only later, primarily under the intellectual leadership of Felix Klein and Hilbert. Almost every leading European mathematician spent some time of his life at Göttingen; it was also a place of pilgrimage for many American mathematicians. The destruction of mathematics in Göttingen by the Nazis, however, shows how fragile a scientific center is. During the two decades after the end of World War II, several first-rate mathematicians have appeared in Germany, but Göttingen, and Germany as a whole, have not regained their former stature in mathematics.

At present there are more first-rate mathematical centers in the United States than in the rest of the world. Nowhere else, with the exception of Moscow and Paris, is there such concentration of leading mathematicians in various fields as in the five to ten leading American universities. Princeton, the Cambridge area, the New York area, the Bay area in California, and Chicago are well recognized as exceptionally strong centers of mathematical life. There are also several strong centers at the great state universities. (The recent rating by the American Council of Education,[32] which lists nine "distinguished" and 16 "strong" departments of mathematics reflects well the general feeling within the mathematical community.)

The strongest mathematical centers play a triple role. They attract some of the most talented undergraduates and in most cases give them an excellent education. In comparison with PhD degree-granting universities generally, they produce a disproportionately large number of PhD's in mathematics, and an even larger percentage of the really outstanding ones. (This is documented in Appendix E.) They also serve as centers for postdoctoral education, either as a major function, as in the case of the Institute for Advanced Study, or, more incidentally, through special research instructorships, terminating assistant professorships, and visiting professorships. Also, most of the outstanding research in mathematical sciences is done at the great centers.*

PHYSICAL MATHEMATICS

An essential task of physical mathematics (sometimes called classical applied mathematics) is to strengthen the intimate interplay between mathematics and the physical sciences for the benefit of both. This is closely connected with teaching and research in the universities, which should provide the appropriate setting in the form of faculty positions or even departments. Although physical mathe-

---

* One should always remember, however, the many exceptional cases. A single outstanding teacher in a place located far from established centers may succeed in educating a large number of research mathematicians. R. L. Moore in Texas is the striking example. A brilliant investigator may make historic discoveries while isolated from a major mathematical community—S. Lefschetz during his Kansas stay, for instance. An important discipline may develop entirely at a secondary place. For example, the recent theory of trigonometric series was mainly created by a large number of workers in a large number of places other than the major centers. See also S. Lefschetz, "A Page of Mathematical Autobiography," *Bull. Amer. Math. Soc., 74,* 854 (1968).

matics is primarily concerned with mathematical physics in general and mechanics in particular, the same spirit can be applied to other mathematical sciences, such as mathematical economics, mathematical biology, and the basic parts of computer science. It is in a comprehensive approach, with a view toward the interplay among the major lines of research, that one can see the most rewards. One may expect that mathematization of new areas in science and technology will result, and that new problems within mathematics itself will be uncovered as well. Thus, the contribution of the physical mathematician to society extends from the very practical aspects of engineering to engineering science, to basic science, and to the stimulation of pure mathematics itself.

Like core mathematics, physical mathematics needs the support of federal funds that will grow in proportion to the growth of the number of workers in the field. The physical mathematician must, however, be concerned with both the mathematical and the scientific aspects of his work; that is, he must bring his theories to the point of comparison with experiments and observations from time to time. This will usually result in a somewhat wider scope of activities (such as extensive numerical computations) and therefore a greater need of funds. In exceptional circumstances, it might even lead to large-scale computing operations. (One such example is Von Neumann's development of numerical weather forecasting.)

Unlike certain other countries, especially Great Britain, the United States lacks a long tradition in physical mathematics. For this reason too, the current level of federal support of this field is not so high as it should be. For a few years, therefore, it may need to grow at a higher rate than the average for all mathematical sciences. There should be a conscious policy of federal support for the research of new faculty members in physical mathematics appointed at the various universities.

Industrial organizations can also provide support for physical mathematicians in the form of research and consultant groups. There is great potential value in the flexibility and breadth of knowledge that the physical mathematician brings to his approach to a number of scientific and technological problems. Some industrial organizations and government laboratories already have excellent mathematical-research groups. Hopefully, for the future we may look forward to the continuation and expansion of such groups.

STATISTICS

Statisticians with research training are needed to fill very different places in our society. First, there is a need for mathematically trained and competent people to develop statistical techniques and evaluate them. Such persons should have an appreciation of how statistical methods are used and what the objectives of statistical applications are. Other statisticians with research training as well as some mathematical competence have great opportunities in positions—academic, industrial, governmental—that involve consulting on the problems of other workers. Many of the great advances have been and still are being made by statisticians of this type. Statisticians who can take operational responsibilities in connection with surveys and other large data-gathering operations—governmental, industrial, or nonprofit—are also badly needed. In their turn, some of them have made basic contributions. Many statisticians operate as individuals within organizations of quite diverse kinds.

There are still great needs for routine work, particularly at the lower levels of survey organizations and in the organizations that spot statisticians singly here and there, but more and more of this is now being done by computers. Statisticians are thus increasingly concerned with innovation. When a problem is posed to him, a statistical consultant may decide that some standard technique can be used; even this often requires innovation in subject-matter concepts. The innovation is more likely, however, to take the form of a newly modified technique. As a consequence, research training is more widely needed than it might seem to be at first sight.

There are demands for new and better formulations of what users of statistics are trying to do, for better and more detailed mathematical treatments of many problems, for the re-examination and modification of many results and techniques to make them more closely matched to the situations in which they are in fact used, for innovation in the form of new techniques, some for wholly new purposes, and for innovation in how modern computing systems are to be put to work (as well as in how their results are to be presented to humans), to name some specific areas. The demands for innovation, coupled with strong demands for many more people with research training to work in a variety of ways, continue to stress research and research training in statistics.

These demands go well beyond what statisticians are presently able to cope with. The weakest link is the number of students qualified and motivated to enter graduate study. We have discussed this problem in the section on Statistics (page 156). Continued expansion of research support is of course essential. As the supply of candidates for graduate study improves, research support may well grow at a somewhat greater rate than in the mathematical sciences proper.

On some campuses, the independent existence of both statistics and computer science poses problems of cooperation and mutual stimulation. On all campuses, making adequate use of modern computing systems in teaching and learning statistics at all levels is of great and growing importance. In this activity, two crucial aspects are: (1) the invention and provision of programming systems that make it easy to do what statisticians have always done to data and, as soon as may be, what statisticians should do to data now that they have modern computing systems, and (2) financing the use of college and university computers by these students.

Most teaching in statistics is "service" teaching, in which the guidelines of the Pierce report,[3] once followed, should provide the needed financing of computer time. Courses predominantly taken by statistics majors, or by potential graduate students in statistics, are likely to require considerably greater contact with modern computing systems, involving correspondingly increased costs. Means for financing such costs are also urgent.

Invention and adaptation of programming systems to meet these needs more effectively is likely to involve elements of research in at least three fields: computer science, statistics, and communication. Support of such research on a selective but diversified basis will be of importance.

As in the case of other frontier fields that are both mathematical sciences and something else, competition for fellowships may be viewed as likely to be unfair to statistics candidates unless statisticians are unusually well represented on the selecting group, and unless these statisticians are sensitive to the extramathematical abilities of the candidates as well as to their mathematical abilities. Changes in practice that make it clear that there are no inequities of this sort would be very worth while. Separate panels for statistics candidates have been suggested; the adequacy of separate panels combining all applied fields of mathematical science where, as noted in the section on Applied Mathematics (page 149), attitudes are desirably different than in core mathematics, probably deserves careful discussion.

COMPUTER SCIENCE

Three related aspects of computer science make it very likely that unusually rapid payoff will result from a heavy investment in research during the next few years. First, it is a field of strikingly rapid growth in which significant theoretical advances are still being made.

Second, because organized complexity is becoming a way of life in the United States, and because computers are well adapted to dealing with such complexity, the solution of many important problems awaits research in computer science. Indeed, there are problems of information processing, vital to many citizens, for which computing systems hold the only foreseeable means of solution. Some striking examples are air and automobile traffic control, management science, information-retrieval problems, and nationwide credit and population records. Of special national concern are applications in medical science, space science, oceanography, weather prediction, and air-defense problems. However, the solution of these and other important problems will come only after extensive research in computer science; building machines is not enough. It has been recognized for several years that the design of efficient programs is even more important than the design of machines.

Third, the computerization of many applications involves large sums of money, so that an increase in effectiveness of even, say, five percent can mean a big saving in just two or three years—an unusually rapid payoff for research—given that the current annual cost of the federal government's acquisition and operation of computers is in the neighborhood of $2 billion.

There is a critical undersupply of leaders in computer science, which has been described at greater length in Chapter 9. Large sums of money go into supplying computing machines to universities and businesses. It is perhaps not widely realized that money for research in computer science is not provided with anywhere near such generosity. We note that the Rosser report[43] sets forth certain dollar figures for the support of research in computer science. We feel that these figures should be regarded as minimal. Because of the great needs for both research itself and for training for leadership through research experience, every effort should be made to support as many good proposals as possible for research in computer science.

While the contributions of industrial research centers are very substantial, it appears likely that for the long-term development of computer science a more academic setting is needed. In many of its activities, university work will be related to the practical software activities of manufacturers in much the same way that work in major engineering schools is presently related to conventional industrial activity. That is, it will deal with aspects of the subject that have the greatest generality and permit some degree of conceptualization.

Research problems in computer science vary widely in character. Many follow the typical pattern of academic research, while a smaller number, including certain very important problems that should be tackled in university environments, require a combination of the academic concern with fundamentals and the industrial capability for organizing substantial group efforts.

The shortage of trained research and teaching staff for academic computer sciences, however it may be structured within the university, is acute. New, badly needed research people must come from varied backgrounds, and the opportunities for sponsored research should include particularly support for young persons of imaginative and experimental bent. The most acute shortage is for research persons with expert knowledge of systems programming.

We find that industry and nonprofit research laboratories have a very substantial number of strong research persons in computer science, including some of the very best. As a result, a much larger fraction of the key research in computer science is done in industry than for the other mathematical sciences. The reasons are clear: (1) nonacademic salaries in these fields, especially for persons just graduating from a university, have been very much higher than those in academic institutions; (2) until the establishment of computer-science departments, there was little or no recognition of the need for teaching of the nonnumerical aspects of computer science in universities; (3) some of the best researchers in the field have not taken PhD degrees and thus appear less desirable to a university than to an industrial laboratory.

It is likely that a substantial number of these persons could be attracted to university teaching and research positions, if these positions were made sufficiently desirable. This would impose a severe strain on university salary scales, a strain that will be uncomfortable but should be faced.

Computing has arrived so fast on the national scene that very little preparation has been made for the organization and financing of research in computer science, instruction in the field, federal financing of fellowships and traineeships, and other matters that have had time to evolve for the older sciences. For this reason it has not been easy to find the agencies with clear responsibility and budget for financing research and education in computer science, though this situation appears to be changing.

Research and education in computer science are substantially more expensive than for most of the mathematical sciences, mainly because they involve access to sophisticated computer systems. We estimate that the over-all annual cost per senior research investigator will be about the same in computer science as in physics, usually ranging from $35,000 to $160,000, with an average near $60,000. The situation is complex because, for economy's sake, the computer systems involved should be integrated with an operating computer center. (Such a center, appropriate to a large university or other organization, is likely to have an initial cost of many millions of dollars.) Moreover, the availability of such computing resources for research and education is usually quite dependent on fundamental accounting policy decisions of the federal government. Some of the issues here are outlined in Appendix D.

The funding of urgently needed space for research in computer science is proving unusually difficult. Money for buildings is always difficult to find in a university, and building projects often have to wait several years to acquire enough priority to demand financial backing. Computer science's very rapid growth makes such delays exceedingly serious.

OPERATIONS RESEARCH AND MANAGEMENT SCIENCE

With the aid of the computer, mathematical methods have been penetrating into every form of human activity. Those that concern the science of decision-making and its application comprise operations research or management science. Essentially, mathematical models are constructed of parts of or sometimes entire industrial and governmental systems, and computers are used to determine optimal schedules or plans. In recent years such applications have grown rapidly. One measure of the practical importance is the cost of computing for linear-programming optimization. This is estimated to be $5 million per year. Development of new computer programs based on established theory runs about $500,000 per new computer system. It is estimated that industry will require 30,000 trained workers in management science in the next few years.

Present financial support of management-science education is geared to only a fraction of this need. Research and training is directed toward analysis of the mathematical structures of typical systems to be optimized. This has stimulated such mathematical disciplines as linear, nonlinear, and integer programming; network, graph, and matroid theory; queueing, stochastic processes, reliability theory; dynamic programming and control theory. Graduate programs have expanded rapidly. An example is the PhD program in operations research at Stanford, which has grown from zero to 50 graduate students in the last six years. Graduate programs are presently limited by the amount of funds available for fellowships, teaching fellowships, and research assistantships. There is a need for greatly increased support of postdoctoral fellows and at least partial support of people in industry and in government who wish to further their knowledge by spending one or two years at a university. There is need of money for experimentation on computers, particularly for testing out new proposals for large-scale system optimization.

OTHER AREAS

Most of the smaller specialized areas, such as mathematical genetics; mathematical psychology; transmission, modulation, and coding theory; and mathematical economics, have been at least reasonably well supported as parts of the respective fields of application in these examples: genetics, psychology, engineering, and economics. This has come about because the value of such work to the field of application has been relatively clear. Since the value of such mathematical areas usually becomes more rather than less clear, research support in these areas will probably increase at a substantial rate, as it should. Moreover, since workers in these areas are usually integrated into academic departments concerned with the discipline of application, a fair number of students with appropriate interests are likely to come in contact with the fields. Thus, graduate-student recruitment is likely to be fairly satisfactory.

Two problems may prove important in individual areas. Departments of mathematics may not adequately recognize the need, at both undergraduate and graduate levels, for new "service courses" of a less usual character. (In certain of these fields, calculus, and the analysis that grows out of it, plays a relatively minor role. Early training in various areas of "discrete mathematics" may be far more important.) Proper evaluation of all facets of the ability of fellowship candidates requires special care.

In other such areas, particularly but not exclusively in those at an early stage of development, other problems may arise. Two seem worthy of notice here: Mathematics may serve as an unwarranted sanction for such projects as the writing of a book on "The Mathematics of X" by a man who gives no evidence of being a good mathematician and who has had no real contact with modern work in X. The converse problem arises when either the mathematics applied or the problem to which it is applied appears too simple, although real gain can come from the application. We are fortunate that this was not the case, for example, in the recent application of mathematical thinking to the description of all possible kinship systems satisfying certain axioms, recently carried out independently by both anthropologically and more mathematically oriented workers. Instances of things appearing too simple are, of course, but specific instances of work that "falls through the crack" by appearing insufficiently interesting both to those working in the discipline and to mathematicians.

No simple prescription can be given to meet these problems. Joint evaluation, of both research projects and fellowship applications, by mathematicians and by workers in the discipline can be of great help, but it is vitally important that those from each of these interests be clearly perceptive of those elements of the other sort of activity that are least natural in their own sort.

Mechanisms that already exist can be of great help in wisely channeling support into new areas and interdisciplinary connections, where intelligent chance-taking is very important for future progress. The Social Science Research Council has a long history of sparking and nurturing important developments in all the behavioral sciences and can be counted on to do well in making selections in all the less highly exploratory areas. The Mathematical Social Sciences Board, though in existence for only three years, has already had very great influence on the rate of progress in the more highly exploratory areas. Both need increased support in their areas of special competence.

In individual universities and colleges, much can be done if individual departments in any of the frontier mathematical fields are encouraged to spread a little outside their nominal boundaries, not only cooperating with workers concerned in various special areas, but becoming involved in joint research or serving as initial homes, wholly or in part, for mathematically oriented faculty not as well housed in their disciplinary departments.

15

The Mathematical Sciences in Society's Service

For wise policy decisions, the tasks and needs of the mathematical sciences, discussed in the previous chapter, must be viewed in proper context. A major element of this context is the whole process by which the mathematical sciences contribute to society's ends. To understand this in full detail would be extremely difficult—probably impossible—but a general overview can be given in reasonable space and with some clarity.

THE MATHEMATICAL POPULATION

The most significant fact about the people and institutions that employ the mathematical sciences, at one level or another, in our society is their number and diversity. Exact figures on the number of our people who have had at least two years of high school mathematics might be hard to find. Rough but probably adequate estimation leads to a figure of perhaps one fourth of the nation's adult population.* With the increasing complexity of society's mechanisms, institutions, and interrelations, leading inevitably to greater public education, this fraction is in the process of slowly moving

---

* According to reference 44, 47.7 percent of the U.S. population over 14 years of age has completed four years of high school and 70.5 percent has completed one through three years of high school. Also, 17.6 percent has completed one through three years of college and 8.1 percent of the population over 14 years of age comprises college graduates.

211

upward. It may well reach one third, one half, and even two thirds as the years pass.

A fundamental education in mathematics extends through high school and about two years of college. Perhaps 8 to 10 million of our people have this foundation, which required 9 to 11 years of study of mathematics. Not all these people make regular use of what they have learned, but a large fraction of those engaged in physical science and engineering do. Altogether, the number who use 11 to 13 years of mathematics, at least occasionally, probably runs between 1 and 2 million.

Now we look at those who work in mathematical sciences in some way or another. The two largest groups are somewhat over 100,000 high school teachers of mathematics and 200,000 computer programmers, to which we should add the roughly 50,000 members of professional societies dealing with mathematical research, college teaching of mathematics, statistics, computer science, operations research, and management science—all told, approximately 350,000 to 400,000 people.

Another group that needs specific notice includes many workers in agricultural, biological, and medical research, many concerned with production or marketing in industry, most research psychologists, and many workers in other fields of behavioral sciences. Some 50,000 to 100,000 such people use statistical methods in their professional work. Many look actively to research in statistical methodology to provide better tools for their use.

Finally, toward the tip of the pyramid there are about 7,000 PhD's in the mathematical sciences, among whom over 1,000 are active innovators. This relatively small group bears the responsibility for practically all research in mathematical sciences, for all research education, and for directing much of the college-level education.

The fraction of our population contained in any of these groups can confidently be expected to increase. Society's increasing complexity and the increasing complexity of its individual mechanisms and institutions will assure this. To estimate the rates of increase, however, is exceedingly difficult, and the figures we now give are only a very rough guess. It seems that the number of people with two years of high school mathematics increases at about 4 percent a year. The pool of those with two or more years of college mathematics grows perhaps 8 percent a year—somewhat more rapidly—while pools of those who use college mathematics may grow as much as 12 percent a year. The numbers of those who use mathematical science as a main professional component grow at diverse annual rates: high school teachers of mathematics at perhaps 5 percent, computer programmers at a rousing 30 percent, professionals at perhaps 14 percent, overall at, say, something over 10 percent. The annual rate of increase of new PhD's over recent years has been 18 percent; as already stated, we believe that active investigators are increasing at about the same percentage per year.

The greater rates of increase at the upper layers of the pyramid are inevitable consequences of the increasing subtlety and complexity of society's demands. An 18 percent annual increase at the research level is no more than would be expected from the other parts of the picture.

We cannot be sure whether the recent rates of growth will or will not continue for the near future. The rate of educating scientifically trained people in each specialty is controlled by students' choices and available facilities. These factors are constantly changing. Over the post-Sputnik decade, enrollments in advanced undergraduate courses in mathematical science grew rapidly, but with a possible tendency to flatten out.* This apparent flattening out may be a short-time fluctuation, may represent limited facilities in terms of faculty, may reflect the absence of undergraduate programs in applied fields, or may be due to a partial reorientation of student values from technical and scientific to social concerns.

Graduate enrollments in mathematical science, particularly at research-training levels, are still growing actively, but their future behavior is equally uncertain. If research training in mathematical science continues to expand rapidly, it will be either because of a continuing atmosphere of general public approval or because we shall have opened the way to graduate work to a wider variety of students by removing social obstacles, by establishing a greater diversity in undergraduate programs, or by broadening understanding and knowledge of mathematical sciences among all college teachers of mathematics. All these reasons for continuing growth are significant and appropriate. If they produce a continuing expansion, the nation has important tasks for all those who will receive research training as a consequence.

* At the same period the engineering numbers flattened out, physics showed moderately strong increases followed by flattening, geology suffered a severe decline followed by a partial recovery, and biology grew, first moderately then more rapidly.

MATHEMATICAL STRATEGY

To assess the significance of research in mathematical sciences from the national point of view, it is important to remember that, as already described in Chapter 3, the strategy of research in mathematics is rather different from that in other sciences.

In nuclear or high-energy physics, for instance, a few problem areas are regarded as crucial at any given time. These are confronted in great force by many people. Substantial numbers of groups of reasonable size, each necessarily well supported by machines of various kinds, attack the same problem. This strategy has brought rapid progress to these areas of physics, probably in part because of the relative narrowness of their research objectives. Even physics in general aims at understanding only one universe, under only one system of laws.

Mathematical research, seen from society's perspective, has a broader objective: the full development of concepts, results, and methods of symbolic reasoning that will apply to as many as possible of mankind's diverse problems, including—vitally but far from exclusively—the problems arising from the progress of physics. The development of concepts and theories motivated by the needs of mathematics itself must be part of this objective since experience shows that these may well become crucially important for applications. As a result, mathematics must contribute to understanding diverse situations under widely different systems of laws.

Mathematical sciences must eventually travel many roads. All past experience, from the dawn of history to recent times, teaches us that the ultimate applicability of a mathematical concept or technique can hardly ever be predicted, that only quite short-range forecasts can be trusted, and that calls for massive effort at one point, at the expense of efforts at other points, should usually be resisted.

In this situation, mathematical sciences proceed by a large number of small independent research efforts, often conducted by single individuals or by small groups of men. A large variety of problems is attacked simultaneously. The choice of problems to work on, as in all sciences, is one of the things that determines the success or failure of an investigator. But the mathematician and the mathematical scientist have, and need, great freedom in making these choices.

This strategy has proved successful. It involves dispersal of forces and active work in many seemingly disconnected fields. Thus there have been repeated periods of apparent overspecialization when mathematicians seemed to be drawing too far from one another (most recently in the 1930's and 1940's). Every time this has happened, however, an apparently inherent unity of mathematics has shown itself again through the appearance of new and more general concepts and approaches that, as in the present decade, have restored to mathematics much more in the way of unity than had seemed possible a few decades earlier.

TRANSFER TIMES

When the British steel industry was renationalized in 1967, the new chairman warned the British people not to expect too much too soon, saying that, in a "capital-intensive" industry, only slow change could be expected. Our nation's system of mathematical service is an institution in which change must be even slower. Indeed, this is a "training-intensive" institution; its greatest investment is in people with years of training. The building of steel plants can be greatly accelerated, but no large group of people can be given 10, or 15, or even 20 years of continuous training in appreciably less than that number of years.

As a language, used for communication both with others and with oneself, mathematics shares with the language of words the need for a long and arduous apprenticeship. Including mathematical training in elementary and secondary school, a college graduate majoring in mathematics has typically studied mathematics about three times as long as a college graduate majoring in a science has studied his or her science. The proper time scale for thinking about our society's system of mathematical science is not merely long, as it must be for all the sciences, but very long.

From society's viewpoint, the largest reason for supporting self-motivated research in mathematical sciences is the continuing impact of the resulting innovations, first as immediate mathematical applications and then more broadly. How fast ought society to expect the results of innovation to be transferred? Surely not in a day or a week or a month. But in one year, or three, or ten?

We have stressed the differences between the strategy of most mathematical research and that of the other sciences and technologies. The individual character of the work and the difficulties of forecasting where progress will prove most important have led to a spreading out of attention over a wide variety of problems. (Important mathematical problems, like many of those posed by David Hilbert in a celebrated 1900 address, are often under attack for several decades before their final solution.) As a consequence of its implicit strategy of pressing ahead wherever it seems that reasonably valuable ground can be gained, mathematical science sometimes prepares the way very far in advance. That important uses should follow discovery by decades, often by several decades, should neither be a cause for surprise nor a reason for criticism. It is a state of affairs intrinsic in an efficient use of human resources and the facilities and money that support them.

A bare trace of our progress in inner-directed research will come to use in one year. A little more will come in three years. A substantial fraction of what will contribute outside mathematical sciences will have begun to make its contribution in 10 years, but only a substantial fraction and only as a beginning. We will do well to do whatever we reasonably can to speed up the process of transfer to use, for there are real gains to be had if we can, but we dare not delude ourselves that great gains in speed can be had by some drastic rearrangement of activity and interest.

The mathematical strategy of widespread attack in small parties is well adapted to both the subject and the demands for innovation laid upon it by the diverse needs of society: long delays in transfer to use are an inevitable consequence of this strategy. In planning support of mathematical sciences, especially support of inner-directed research, we must take the long view if our programs are to contribute to the demands that society will make at times spread through the future.

We do many other things today with a hope of social gain over decades. The elementary and high school education of youth is to be of value to them and to society, not just for a decade or two, but for four or five or even six decades. All our affairs cannot be conducted in the way a field of corn is tended, plowed under this year but reseeded for next year. Innovation in science is more like an apple tree; 10 to 25 years are needed for the crop to return, many-fold, the effort of planting, grafting, and cultivation. Mathematical sciences call for time scales even longer than do other sciences.

EMERGENCIES

There is an exception to the usual need for long transfer times typical in the mathematical sciences—the use of creative mathematicians during emergencies.

World War II generated many technical emergencies. Mathematicians usually involved in inner-directed research responded to many calls: how to conduct antisubmarine warfare, what principles to use in fighter and bomber gunsights, and many questions in ballistics, radar, atomic weapons, and cryptography. The crisis was clear; insight, knowledge, and skill were freely mobilized. Many concrete problems whose solution was explicitly demanded were attacked powerfully and effectively by mathematicians, precisely because of their professional ability and training in thinking into the heart of a problem and seizing on its essentials. And the free-wheeling instinct of the self-motivated researcher played its part.

Another emergency arose slowly and imperceptibly in mathematical education, primarily in elementary schols and high schools. The urgent need for reform became apparent about 15 years ago. Leadership in meeting this emergency came in a large measure from university and college mathematicians active in inner-directed research. There are various opinions in the mathematical community about the success of the reform movement thus far; there is no dispute about the necessity of curriculum reform.) When the next major change in mathematical education comes, leadership will again have to be drawn from those concerned with inner-directed research.

Mathematical scientists who give most of their time to inner-directed research are an important national resource in emergencies. This sort of resource serves special purposes in an emergency, but it cannot be used for these purposes steadily. This type of value has to be a by-product. As long as emergencies continue to arise at the usual rate, society can count on this resource created by basic mathematical research as one sort of return from its investments in research training in mathematical science. It can do this, however, only by using research-trained people quite differently most of the time.

THE LEVEL OF INVESTMENT

We are now in a position to ask whether the total investment in basic mathematical research has been at a reasonable level. Let us follow our discussion of Level and Sources of Support (see page 163) and assume federal support of basic research in the universities as $35 million in 1966. At an 18 percent rate of growth, the total through all the past would be about six times as large as the present annual amount, amounting to $200 million. Allowance for non-federal support and for slower rates of growth in the past might raise this to $250 million. If we believe in compound interest, and insist on totaling up present values of all sums spent in the past, this figure would be roughly $300 million.

Thus, if we want a total investment picture, we can say that the whole U.S. investment in research in the mathematical sciences to date is about as much as we will spend as initial capital investment on the new super-large "atom-smasher" now approved. When we look at this investment in mathematical research as contributing in diverse and important ways to the effectiveness of the whole national system of mathematical service, where some of these ways have begun, others are beginning, and others will start at times spread forward through decades, and where most contributions will continue for a long time, our investment seems conservative and cautious, perhaps disproportionately small.

GROWTH CANNOT BE FOREVER

An 18 percent a year increase means doubling every four years. A 10 percent annual increase means doubling in less than 10 years. Such doubling cannot continue indefinitely. Not only mathematical science but all science and all technologies with growing research sectors must face the need for an ultimate tapering off. Neither the fraction of gross national product that can be devoted to research nor the number of people potentially capable of becoming research investigators can increase indefinitely.

At the moment, the need for the innovations of mathematical science research is large and growing. These needs would require continuing rapid expansion for the near future, even without the necessity of continuing the mathematical teaching of nonprofessionals. But what of the day when tapering off of growth becomes appropriate? What will be the environment, the pressures, the appropriate adjustments?

Education above the high school level is in transition. The classical division between undergraduate and graduate work is more and more clearly seen to be at an inappropriate place. We may be moving toward a three-part scheme of scientific education, consisting of (1) the present freshman and sophomore years, (2) the last two undergraduate years and graduate study through the comprehensive examination, and (3) thesis research and postdoctoral training. It will be after this pattern has appeared more clearly that we shall have to face declining rates of increase in supported research.

At present, five sixths of new PhD's follow career patterns that do not lead to federally supported research. If our needs for professionally trained personnel were to cease to rise, adjustments would be fairly simple. If, as seems more likely, the future demand for professionally trained personnel increases much more than in proportion to the amount of sponsored research that the nation can afford, there will have to be major readjustments.

Direct contact with research leadership contributes greatly to education in mathematical sciences below the research level. In the future, research leaders may not be able to contribute much time to this activity. Once this situation arises, forms of mass communication, both television and film, will become important in the process, and there will have to be real innovations designed to provide face-to-face contact with many students.

Inevitably, the selection of a principal investigator for research support will focus increasingly on the number and quality of his PhD candidates, as well as on the number and quality of his own contributions. As a consequence, it will become clearer that academic tenure exists primarily for teaching rather than for research support.

Such times, when they come to each science, will be times of change indeed. There are many reasons, however, why they will not come to all sciences together. The bigger the initial budget, the sooner its doubling will bring it to a point where things must be done. The larger the system of activities that research in a science supports, the larger the total the nation can wisely spend on it.

Today, academic mathematical research receives a relatively small amount of support—less than three cents out of every dollar spent by the federal government for research at universities. Yet this mathematical research is the leading wedge of a very large national effort. Thus, reduction of growth rate in mathematical research ought, wisely and advisedly, to take place only after similar reductions have been made in many other fields. Thus the mathematical sciences can expect much guidance by the time they are faced with making their own adjustments.

THE NONUTILITARIAN VIEW

Our report would put the research activities of mathematical science in distorted context if it were to give the impression that all society's demands on mathematical science are utilitarian—a vivid untruth.

As many nonmathematicians know, the central constructions of mathematics are among the noblest creations of the human spirit. For millennia this has been true of mathematics as well as of poetry and music.

Were there no demands for the ultimately useful, society would not choose to be wholly without mathematics. It would continue to value mathematics for intellectual strength and beauty. The appeal that mathematics has for its practitioners, in particular for research mathematicians, is largely aesthetic. The joy experienced in learning and in creating mathematics is akin to that associated with art and poetry. This joy, however, can be shared only by relatively few people and requires an apprenticeship. Still, the number of people able to enjoy mathematics is rapidly growing, as shown by the unexpectedly large sales of popular books on mathematics. Society would hardly support, on grounds of intellectual achievement and appeal alone, the volume of research in the mathematical sciences appropriate to its other ends; but society would always find ways to keep this intellectual activity alive.

References

1. Panel on Undergraduate Education of the Committee on Support of Research in the Mathematical Sciences, *The Mathematical Sciences: Undergraduate Education*, NAS Publ. 1682, National Academy of Sciences, Washington, D.C. (1968).

2. *Federal Funds for Research, Development and Other Scientific Activities*, National Science Foundation.

3. President's Science Advisory Committee, Panel on Computers in Education, John R. Pierce, Chairman, *Computers in Higher Education*, U.S. Govt. Printing Office, Washington, D.C. (1967).

4. "Resolutions Addressed to the Congress of the United States and to the Officers of the National Science Foundation by the Mathematical Association of America," *Amer. Math. Mon., 74*, 473–475 (1967).

5. Leonard Gillman and Don Thomson, "Summer Institutes for College Teachers," *Amer. Math. Mon., 74*, 316–317 (1967).

6. Committee for the Survey of Chemistry, Frank H. Westheimer, Chairman, *Chemistry: Opportunities and Needs*, NAS-NRC Publ. 1292, National Academy of Sciences–National Research Council, Washington, D.C. (1966).

7. *The Mathematical Sciences: A Collection of Essays*, compiled by the Committee on Support of Research in the Mathematical Sciences with the editorial collaboration of G. A. W. Boehm, published for the National Academy of Sciences, Washington, D.C., by The MIT Press, Cambridge, Mass. (1969).

8. Thornton C. Fry, "Industrial Mathematics," reprint from a House document of the 77th Congress, *Research—A National Resource—II*, from Section VI, Part 4, pp. 268–288 (1940).

9. F. J. Weyl, *Report on a Survey of Training and Research in Applied Mathematics in the United States*, Society for Industrial and Applied Mathematics, Philadelphia, Pa. (1956).

10. Hermann Weyl, *Symmetry*, Princeton University Press, Princeton, N.J. (1952).

11. Physics Survey Committee, *Physics: Survey and Outlook, Reports on the Subfields of Physics*, NAS-NRC Publ. 1295A, National Academy of Sciences–National Research Council, Washington, D.C. (1966).

12. L. F. Richardson, *Weather Prediction by Numerical Process* (1922), reprinted by Dover Publications, Inc., New York (1965).

13. R. Bush, E. Galanter, and R. D. Luce, editors, *Handbook of Mathematical Psychology, Volumes I–III*, John Wiley & Sons, Inc., New York (1963).

14. R. M. Thrall, J. A. Mortimer, K. B. Rebman, and R. F. Baum, compilers and editors, *Some Mathematical Models in Biology*, The University of Michigan, Ann Arbor, Mich. (1967).

15. Clarence B. Lindquist, *Mathematics in Colleges & Universities: A Comprehensive Survey of Graduate and Undergraduate Programs (Final Report)*, OE-56018, U.S. Govt. Printing Office, Washington, D.C. (1965).

16. Report of the Survey Committee, Conference Board of the Mathematical Sciences, *Volume I, Aspects of Undergraduate Training in the Mathematical Sciences* (1967); Volume II (in preparation); Volume III (in preparation).

17. Kenneth A. Simon and Marie G. Fullam, *Projections of Educational Statistics to 1975–76*, OE-10030, U.S. Govt. Printing Office, Washington, D.C. (1966).

18. *Earned Degrees Conferred by Institutions of Higher Education* (specifically the reports for the years 1954–55 through 1963–64), USOE reports, U.S. Govt. Printing Office, Washington, D.C. (1956–1965).

19. Committee on the Undergraduate Program in Mathematics, *Recommendations on the Undergraduate Mathematics Program for Engineers and Physicists*, Mathematical Association of America, Buffalo, N.Y. (1962).

20. Committee on the Undergraduate Program in Mathematics, *A Curriculum in Applied Mathematics*, Mathematical Association of America, Buffalo, N.Y. (1966).

21. Committee on the Undergraduate Program in Mathematics, *Tentative Recommendations for the Undergraduate Mathematics Program of Students in the Biological, Management and Social Sciences*, Mathematical Association of America, Buffalo, N.Y. (1964).

22. Committee on the Undergraduate Program in Mathematics, *Recommendations on the Undergraduate Mathematics Program for Work in Computing*, Mathematical Association of America, Buffalo, N.Y. (1964).

23. Committee on the Undergraduate Program in Mathematics, *Recommendations for the Training of Teachers of Mathematics*, Mathematical Association of America, Buffalo, N.Y. (1966).

24. American Society for Engineering Education, *Goals of Engineering Education: The Preliminary Report*, ASEE, Washington, D.C. (1965).

25. Committee on the Undergraduate Program in Mathematics, *Forty-One Conferences on the Training of Teachers of Elementary School Mathematics: A Summary*, Harold T. Slaby, editor, Mathematical Association of America, Buffalo, N.Y. (1966).

26. Allan M. Cartter, "Future Faculty Needs and Resources," in *Improving College Teaching*, American Council on Education, Washington, D.C. (1966).

27. Allan M. Cartter, "A New Look at the Supply of College Teachers," *Educ. Rec.*, pp. 267–277 (Summer 1965).

28. *Opening Fall Enrollments in Higher Education, 1966*, OE-54003-66, U.S. Govt. Printing Office, Washington, D.C. (1967).

29. Committee on the Undergraduate Program in Mathematics, *Qualifications for a College Faculty in Mathematics: Report of the Ad Hoc Committee on*

the Qualifications of College Teachers, Mathematical Association of America, Buffalo, N.Y. (1967).

30. *Scientists, Engineers, and Technicians in the 1960's: Requirements and Supply,* NSF 63–34, U.S. Govt. Printing Office, Washington, D.C. (1963).

31. *Employment in Professional Mathematical Work in Industry and Government,* NSF 62–12, U.S. Govt. Printing Office, Washington, D.C. (1962).

32. Allan M. Cartter, *An Assessment of Quality in Graduate Education,* American Council on Education, Washington, D.C. (1966).

33. Committee on the Undergraduate Program in Mathematics, reports on CUPM regional conferences, Mathematical Association of America, Buffalo, N.Y. (1966 and 1967).

34. Allan Tucker, David Gottlieb, and John Pease, *Attrition of Graduate Students at the Ph.D. Level in the Traditional Arts and Sciences,* Michigan State University, East Lansing, Mich. (1964).

35. Education in Applied Mathematics: Proceedings of a Conference Sponsored by the Society for Industrial and Applied Mathematics, *SIAM Rev.,* pp. 289–415 (April 1967).

36. "Curriculum 68: Recommendations for Academic Programs in Computer Science," *Commun. Assoc. Computing Mach., 11,* 151–197 (1968).

37. G. E. Forsythe, "A University's Educational Program in Computer Science," *Commun. Assoc. Computing Mach., 10,* 3–11 (1967).

38. H. Kanter, A. Moore, and N. Singer, "The Allocation of Computer Time by University Computer Centers," *J. Business* (April 1968).

39. Committee on Applied Mathematical Statistics, *Personnel and Training Problems Created by the Recent Growth of Applied Statistics in the United States,* NRC Reprint and Circular Series, No. 128, National Research Council, Washington, D.C. (1947).

40. Harvey Brooks, "Applied Science and Technological Progress," *Science, 156,* 1706–1712 (1967).

41. Committee on Science and Public Policy, *Federal Support of Basic Research in Institutions of Higher Learning,* NAS-NRC Publ. 1185, National Academy of Sciences–National Research Council, Washington, D.C. (1964).

42. Physics Survey Committee, George E. Pake, Chairman, *Physics: Survey and Outlook, A Report on the Present State of U.S. Physics and Its Requirements for Future Growth,* NAS-NRC Publ. 1295, National Academy of Sciences–National Research Council, Washington, D.C. (1966).

43. Committee on Uses of Computers, J. Barkley Rosser, Chairman, *Digital Computer Needs in Universities and Colleges,* NAS-NRC Publ. 1233, National Academy of Sciences–National Research Council, Washington, D.C. (1966).

44. *A Fact Book on Higher Education,* American Council on Education, Washington, D.C. (1967).

Appendixes

Appendix A

Individuals Who Contributed to the Work of COSRIMS*

COSRIMS

Lipman Bers, *Columbia University*, Chairman
T. W. Anderson, *Columbia University*
R. H. Bing, *University of Wisconsin*
Hendrik W. Bode, *Bell Telephone Laboratories*
R. P. Dilworth, *California Institute of Technology*
George E. Forsythe, *Stanford University*
Mark Kac, *Rockefeller University*
C. C. Lin, *Massachusetts Institute of Technology*
John W. Tukey, *Princeton University*
F. J. Weyl, *National Academy of Sciences*
Hassler Whitney, *Institute for Advanced Study*
C. N. Yang, *State University of New York at Stony Brook*
Truman Botts, *University of Virginia*, Executive Director

Leon W. Cohen, *Division of Mathematical Sciences, National Research Council*, Liaison Representative
Dorothy M. Gilford, *Department of Defense*, Liaison Representative
William H. Pell, *National Science Foundation*, Liaison Representative
Milton E. Rose, *National Science Foundation*, Liaison Representative

* In each case, the affiliation indicated is the one covering most of the time when COSRIMS was active.

227

George A. W. Boehm, Editorial Consultant
Lynnel M. Garabedian, Administrative Assistant

PANEL ON APPLIED MATHEMATICS

Stanislaw Ulam, *University of Colorado,* Chairman
George Carrier, *Harvard University*
Harold Grad, *New York University*
C. C. Lin, *Massachusetts Institute of Technology*
Allen Newell, *Carnegie Institute of Technology*
William Prager, *University of California, San Diego*
John W. Tukey, *Princeton University*
Howard Raiffa, *Harvard University*
C. N. Yang, *State University of New York at Stony Brook*
L. A. Zadeh, *University of California, Berkeley*
Norman J. Zabusky, *Bell Telephone Laboratories*

PANEL ON GRADUATE EDUCATION

Ralph P. Boas, *Northwestern University,* Chairman
R. D. Anderson, *Louisiana State University*
David Blackwell, *University of California, Berkeley*
Felix Browder, *University of Chicago*
R. C. Buck, *University of Wisconsin*
S. S. Chern, *University of California, Berkeley*
Philip J. Davis, *Brown University*
Wilfrid Dixon, *University of California, Los Angeles*
George E. Forsythe, *Stanford University*
I. N. Herstein, *University of Chicago*
Peter J. Hilton, *Cornell University*
William Miller, *Stanford University*
Dorothy M. Stone, *University of Rochester*

PANEL ON LEVEL AND FORMS OF SUPPORT

Mina S. Rees, *City University of New York,* Chairman
Morton Curtis, *Rice University*
Mahlon M. Day, *University of Illinois*
L. H. Farinholt, *Sloan Foundation*
Andrew W. Gleason, *Harvard University*
J. P. LaSalle, *Brown University*
F. J. Weyl, *National Academy of Sciences*

PANEL ON NEW CENTERS

Mark Kac, *Rockefeller University,* Chairman
R. D. Anderson, *Louisiana State University*

R. H. Bing, *University of Wisconsin*
Charles W. Curtis, *University of Oregon*
Saunders Mac Lane, *University of Chicago*

PANEL ON PURE MATHEMATICS

A. Adrian Albert, *University of Chicago,* Chairman
Raoul Bott, *Harvard University*
Stephen Kleene, *University of Wisconsin*
Saunders Mac Lane, *University of Chicago*
Deane Montgomery, *Institute for Advanced Study*
Charles B. Morrey, Jr., *University of California, Berkeley*

PANEL ON UNDERGRADUATE EDUCATION

John G. Kemeny, *Dartmouth College,* Chairman
Grace E. Bates, *Mount Holyoke College*
D. E. Christie, *Bowdoin College*
Llayron Clarkson, *Texas Southern University*
George Handelman, *Rensselaer Polytechnic Institute*
Frederick Mosteller, *Harvard University*
Henry Pollak, *Bell Telephone Laboratories*
Hartley Rogers, *Massachusetts Institute of Technology*
John Toll, *State University of New York at Stony Brook*
Robert J. Wisner, *New Mexico State University*

COSRIMS–CBMS SURVEY PANEL ON THE MATHEMATICAL SCIENCES IN
INDUSTRY AND GOVERNMENT

J. P. LaSalle, *Brown University,* Chairman
B. H. Colvin, *Boeing Scientific Research Laboratories*
Ralph E. Gomory, *International Business Machines Corporation*
Mario L. Juncosa, RAND *Corporation*
John R. Rice, *Purdue University*
Milton E. Rose, *National Science Foundation*
Robert F. Wheeling, *Mobil Oil Corporation*
John W. Wrench, Jr., *David Taylor Model Basin*
Edward E. Zajac, *Bell Telephone Laboratories*

AUTHORS OF COSRIMS ESSAYS

Lipman Bers, *Columbia University*
R. H. Bing, *University of Wisconsin*
Hirsh Cohen, *International Business Machines Corporation*

H. S. M. Coxeter, *University of Toronto*
Philip J. Davis, *Brown University*
Freeman Dyson, *Institute for Advanced Study*
Samuel Eilenberg, *Columbia University*
George E. Forsythe, *Stanford University*
Andrew W. Gleason, *Harvard University*
Zellig Harris, *University of Pennsylvania*
Mark Kac, *Rockefeller University*
John G. Kemeny, *Dartmouth College*
Jack Kiefer, *Cornell University*
Lawrence R. Klein, *University of Pennsylvania*
Joshua Lederberg, *Stanford University*
E. J. McShane, *University of Virginia*
Gian-Carlo Rota, *Massachusetts Institute of Technology*
Jacob T. Schwartz, *New York University*
Raymond Smullyan, *Yeshiva University*
Stanislaw Ulam, *University of Colorado*
A. S. Wightman, *Princeton University*

CONFERENCE BOARD OF MATHEMATICAL SCIENCES (CBMS) SURVEY COMMITTEE

Gail S. Young, *Tulane University*, Chairman
Leon W. Cohen, *University of Maryland*
William L. Duren, *University of Virginia*
Herman H. Goldstine, *International Business Machines Corporation*
J. P. LaSalle, *Brown University*
W. T. Martin, *Massachusetts Institute of Technology*
George E. Nicholson, *University of North Carolina*
Lowell J. Paige, *University of California, Los Angeles*
Henry Pollak, *Bell Telephone Laboratories*
Stephen S. Willoughby, *New York University*
John Jewett, *Oklahoma State University*, Executive Director

CBMS SURVEY PANEL ON GRADUATE EDUCATION

Lowell J. Paige, *University of California, Los Angeles*, Chairman
Henry A. Antosiewicz, *University of Southern California*
Harvey Cohn, *University of Arizona*
Robert P. Dilworth, *California Institute of Technology*
Lester H. Lange, *San Jose State College*

CBMS SURVEY PANEL ON INFORMATION SCIENCE

Herman H. Goldstine, *International Business Machines Corporation*, Chairman
Robert L. Ashenhurst, *University of Chicago*

William F. Atchison, *University of Maryland*
Hirsh G. Cohen, *International Business Machines Corporation*
Bruce Gilchrist, *International Business Machines Corporation*
Thomas A. Keenan, EDUCOM, *Bethesda, Maryland*
William B. Kehl, *Massachusetts Institute of Technology*

CBMS SURVEY PANEL ON MATHEMATICS EDUCATION

Stephen S. Willoughby, *New York University,* Chairman
Julius H. Hlavaty, *National Council of Teachers of Mathematics*
Burton W. Jones, *University of Colorado*
Peter D. Lax, *New York University*
Bruce E. Meserve, *University of Vermont*

CBMS SURVEY PANEL ON PROBABILITY AND STATISTICS

George E. Nicholson, *University of North Carolina,* Chairman
T. W. Anderson, *Columbia University*
William Kruskal, *University of Chicago*
John Tukey, *Princeton University*

OTHER CONTRIBUTORS

Merle Andrew, *Air Force Office of Scientific Research*
William F. Atchison, *University of Maryland*
Hyman Bass, *Columbia University*
Edward G. Begle, *Stanford University*
Carl Bennett, *Battelle Memorial Institute*
Carl Borgman, *Ford Foundation*
Robin Bostick, *The Rockefeller University*
Leila Bram, *Office of Naval Research*
Harvey Brooks, *Harvard University*
James E. Burnett, *Columbia University*
Allan M. Cartter, *New York University*
Noam Chomsky, *Massachusetts Institute of Technology*
Raymond S. Craig, *University of Pittsburgh*
William Craig, *University of California, Berkeley*
Henry David, *National Academy of Sciences*
James W. Dow, *National Institutes of Health*
Merrill M. Flood, *University of Michigan*
John K. Folger, *Commission of Human Resources and Advanced Education*
Karl M. Folley, *Wayne State University*
Robert A. Foster, *Columbia University*
Fred Frishman, *U.S. Army Research Office*
A. S. Galbraith, *U.S. Army Research Office*
Patrick X. Gallagher, *Columbia University*

Leonard Gillman, *University of Rochester*
Wallace Givens, *Argonne National Laboratory*
Robert E. Green, *National Academy of Sciences*
Herbert Greenberg, *University of Denver*
Walter A. Hahn, *Environmental Science Services Administration*
John W. Hamblen, *Southern Regional Education Board*
Lindsey R. Harmon, *National Academy of Sciences*
Geoffrey Keller, *National Science Foundation*
Steven L. Kleiman, *Columbia University*
Ellis R. Kolchin, *Columbia University*
Walter L. Koltun, *National Science Foundation*
Ralph Krause, *National Science Foundation*
T. R. Jenkins, *Lockheed Palo Alto Research Laboratory*
Elizabeth La Jeunesse, *Bell Telephone Laboratories*
Herbert D. Landahl, *University of Chicago*
C. J. Lapp, *National Academy of Sciences*
James Lighthill, *University of London*
Clarence B. Lindquist, *U.S. Office of Education*
Murray Mannos, *Mitre Corporation*
Constance Messer, *American Mathematical Society*
E. P. Miles, *Florida State University*
George Miller, *Harvard University*
G. H. Miller, *Tennessee Technological University*
Marion B. Miller, *American Mathematical Society*
Jean B. Morales, *University of California*
Manuel F. Morales, *University of California*
Robert W. Murdock, *Lindenwood College*
Morris Newman, *National Bureau of Standards*
Michael J. Norris, *Sandia Corporation Laboratory*
Harold Orlans, *Brookings Institution*
Robert H. Owens, *University of Virginia*
Russell Phelps, *National Science Foundation*
Alan J. Perlis, *Carnegie-Mellon University*
Billy J. Pettis, *University of North Carolina*
Everett Pitcher, *Lehigh University*
Malcolm W. Pownall, *Committee on the Undergraduate Program in Mathematics*
Donald K. Price, *Harvard University*
Henry S. Reuss, *United States House of Representatives*
David Rosen, *Swarthmore College*
Thomas L. Saaty, *Conference Board of the Mathematical Sciences*
Frederick G. Shuman, *National Meteorological Center*
Joseph Smagorinsky, *Geophysical Fluid Dynamics Laboratory*
Herbert Solomon, *Stanford University*
Bernard R. Stein, *National Science Foundation*
Fern Steininger, *National Academy of Sciences*
Sol Swerdloff, *Bureau of Labor Statistics, U.S. Department of Labor*
Allan Tucker, *State University System of Florida*
Gordon Walker, *American Mathematical Society*

Appendix B

Final Report of the American Mathematical Society's Committee on Information Exchange and Publication in Mathematics*

I. The original charge to this committee was to ask the right questions about communications in mathematics, questions whose answers would provide the information necessary for deciding on future action by mathematics organizations. There was some indication that if such questions could be pinpointed, then the NSF might be willing to help in getting the answers. It turned out that the concrete implementation of this would probably mean conducting a large survey of mathematicians, mainly in the form of questionnaires. It turned out further that the NSF was not in a position to offer any help except to comment on professional survey organizations which might be able to conduct such a survey.

After considering this matter for many months, and after informal contact with two of the most reputable academic-type survey organizations (The Survey Research Center at the University of Chicago, for one), we concluded that a large survey would be a waste of energy and would provide much more irritation to the mathematicians questioned than it would provide sound information to the questioners. Such a survey could, at most, tell what is happening now, but it is more likely to tell what people think is happening now; the results of such a survey are too easily rigged by the selection of the questions or the persons questioned; in short, the survey idea seemed a poor basis for future action. Furthermore, there have been numerous studies of information exchange in various sciences in recent years [see *The Flow of (Behavioral) Science Information—A Review*

---

* Reproduced by permission.

of the Research Library, by William J. Paisley, Institute for Communication Research, Stanford University, November 1965, which lists at least 29 studies between 1948 and 1965] and all these studies seem to come to much the same conclusions as we would have predicted on the basis of "pure thought." The proposal to abandon the idea of a survey seems to have met with the approval of all parties involved in setting up the original charge to this committee.

We therefore recommend that the American Mathematical Society set up a permanent committee to monitor problems of communication; that this committee should experiment with pilot projects in (hopefully) improved modes of communication if such projects are approved by the AMS and other societies concerned; and that the results of these experiments be carefully assessed after a suitable trial period. This committee should have some members representing the more applied areas of mathematics and it should work in close liaison with the other mathematical organizations, including CBMS. We have spelled out below some of the relevant areas and some projects we think could be followed up immediately. Specifically, we feel that the Information Center described in Part II, the repository in Part III, and the Proposal for Writing Panels in Applied Mathematics in Part V are especially worthy of present attention.

II. Prepublication services. The present methods of journal publication are threatening to become unmanageable as the number of journals and the number of papers increases. The years 1950–1965 have already seen an increase of about 250 percent in the number of pages and the number of papers published. Judging from the numbers of new PhD's in mathematics, this rate of growth is not likely to decrease. Our committee did not feel that making these results available with great speed was of primary importance. Our present time lag in publication of from one to two years is much too long, but decreasing this is not a primary problem. Suggestions for avoiding the avalanche which seems to be coming should aim to make any one piece of research more readily visible to those who need it, and to make it easily accessible. After all, each mathematician has only a finite amount of time and energy to devote to learning new results and it is most important to help him use this time effectively.

It is standard practice now to communicate results of research before publication. Many organizations have tried to formalize this system of preprints. The National Institutes of Health organized nine Information Exchange Groups in various aspects of biology; each group consisted of from 100 to 1500 research personnel, each of whom automatically received all preprints submitted by other members of his group. These groups have recently been discontinued by the NIH, though they hope other organizations will continue the system [see *Science, 154,* 843 (18 November 1966)]. One of the American Chemical Society's applied journals, *Industrial and Engineering Chemistry,* has been publishing 50-word abstracts of all papers being refereed and will sell copies of the manuscripts to anyone who is interested. The AMS has considered publishing lists of titles of all forthcoming papers. The Category Information Centre has recently been organized to distribute information on the whereabouts of mathematicians interested in category theory, and on the results they prove. The actual functioning of this organization is not yet clear to us.

Our committee suggests that such semiformal prepublication communication is worthwhile and should be encouraged. It is probably better to have some organization handling preprints than to depend on each author's private distribution lists as at present. It is not clear what encouragement the Category Information Centre (centered in Prague) would desire, but similar centers might be organized in one or more other fields of mathematics, for example, in numerical solutions of partial differential equations, or in differential topology, or in operator theory (Hilbert space), or in set theory. Such a center might be restricted to distributing bibliographical information or it might actually sell copies of manuscripts which are submitted to it. We doubt that the automatic distribution (as in NIH's IEG's) is worthwhile for papers which have not yet been refereed. It is also important to be sure that all this transitory material eventually disappears. Correct bibliographical references should be made available to all participants when a preprint is published. The experience of *Industrial and Engineering Chemistry* is that distributing copies of the manuscript is rather expensive, but it is conceivable that it could be automated if the demand were great enough. If such centers are set up, they will have to be reviewed periodically in some objective way to see if they are, in fact, improving the communication among mathematicians.

III. Modes of publication. Publication of research articles will probably have to be changed in some manner or other eventually.

Our committee kept returning to the suggestion that some journal, for example the *Bulletin* or the *Proceedings* of the American Mathematical Society, be devoted exclusively to publication of two-page abstracts of papers, after these abstracts have been refereed by a competent mathematician who has access to the full text of the manuscript. Some central repository would collect these manuscripts. Any interested mathematician could receive a copy of the full manuscript by requesting it from this repository. It should be made extremely easy to submit such requests. In fact, eventually this might be done by punching a few buttons on an electronic console which will then produce a hard copy of the manuscript a few minutes later. However, at present the mails are probably still adequate. For example, as a privilege of his subscription, a mathematician might receive a number of coupons which could be torn off and mailed to the repository, thereby automatically requesting a specific article. Publication of such an abstract would count as publication, since the paper is refereed and available in full to interested readers with reasonable ease. To implement such a scheme, it would be important to raise standards of publication in all other journals. This might be easier than merely raising standards a little bit. More journals could then devote much space to survey articles at a very high level, supplementing the present activities of the *Bulletin*.

Aside from provision for such survey articles, the American Mathematical Society could drastically cut the page allotments in its present journals and might well enlist the cooperation of most other American journals. If this results in a major overflow into foreign journals, they might also be tempted to join in such a program of publication by abstract. Presumably both the by-title abstracts in the *Notices* and the research announcements in the *Bulletin* could then be eliminated; perhaps all the abstracts could go.

This is an ambitious scheme, but with support from the NSF to help temporarily in the reproduction and distribution costs, it might even work for a long enough time to determine whether it could serve the needs of mathematics.

On a smaller scale, the MAA is toying with the idea of changing the *Monthly* in part to a collection of abstracts. Cooperation and observation here might also be in order.

An alternative to this repository scheme is the publication of a journal of abstracts with the total manuscript reduced to microfiche possibly even accompanying the journal. The *Mathematics of Computation* is now considering a microfiche supplement to their journal which might include the texts of tables reviewed in the journal or other extensions of the printed text. It would be interesting to cooperate in this experiment and assess the results after about two years.

IV.   Retrieval. We should take advantage of experiments in information retrieval now being tried in mathematics and other disciplines and assess their relevance and value to mathematics as a whole. Among such experiments we should list the following:

1. *Citation Index.* This associates to each published paper all the subsequent papers which refer to it in their bibliographies. Such a citation index is being constructed at UCLA for current mathematics and another is being constructed by Tukey and others for past and present probability and statistics.

2. *Permuted Index.* This type of index is most easily described by the sample page (shown in Figure B1) from an index of the approximately 1500 papers appearing in the *Transactions* of the American Mathematical Society from Volume 86 (1956) to Volume 104 (1962). The left-hand column gives the date and a code for the author's name (this code is translated in a separate index). The second and third columns are the standard volume and page references, and the rest consists of titles arranged alphabetically according to one word of the title. Apparently each title is indexed under each word in it except for prepositions and conjunctions. The Permuted Index for the *Transactions,* including a chronological list of papers and the author index is a pile of standard IBM sheets about ⅜ inch thick (if you don't squeeze too hard). Apparently the Association for Computing Machinery publishes such a permuted index to *Computing Reviews* at about three-year intervals. Presumably Aaron Feineman at Stony Brook knows most about its effectiveness.

3. The *MAC* Technical Information project at MIT includes a combination of Permuted Index and a Citation Index stored in a computer so that the retrieval of the information (title, author or citation) is done by machine.

4. *Mathematical Reviews subject index.*

5. The volume of reviews in differential topology which the AMS is now preparing under the direction of Steenrod.

BLEMS FOR THE DIFFERENTIAL EQUATION LX = LAMBDA 58BRR 88TAMS 331
ON CONJUGATE SPACES OF 59YMO 90TAMS 291
OGUES OF THE GROUP OF PERMUTATIONS OF THE 62KNT 104TAMS 347
59PLS 92TAMS 125
SOME SEMIGROUPS ON AN 61HON 99TAMS 255
A TYPE OF CONVEXITY IN THE SPACE OF 56DLW 83TAMS 193
EM ON ENTIRE FUNCTIONS. 56RBL 83TAMS 417
MUM PRINCIPLE FOR HYPERBOLIC EQUATIONS IN A 58PRR 87TAMS 119
AN ANALYSIS OF THE WANG ALGEBRA OF 61HHN 99TAMS 114
LOCALLY AFFINE SPACES WITH 61SZI 99TAMS 425
FINITE GROUPS WITH 62SNL 103TAMS 516
A SUBGROUP THEOREM FOR FREE 62MRN 103TAMS 495
ME IMBEDDING AND NONIMBEDDING THEOREMS FOR 62STD 103TAMS 403
RAS OF CHARACTERISTIC P. 60SCR 94TAMS 310
ARY INTERSECTIONS FOR TWO SIDED IDEALS OF A 59FLR 90TAMS 336
OVERRINGS OF COMMUTATIVE RINGS. I. 62DVS 104TAMS 52
HOMOLOGICAL DIMENSION IN 58ASR 88TAMS 194
INJECTIVE DIMENSION IN 62AAS 102TAMS 18
DIFFERENTIAL EQUATIONS WITH/ ON LINEAR AND 56HRN 81TAMS LNPL
TAU = U POUR CERTAINNES CLASSES D' OPERATEURS 57FIS 86TAMS 335
PRIME IDEALS IN 58BRN 69TAMS 245
A CLASS OF 58CNN 89TAMS 395
S — A FAITHFUL REPRESENTATION OF PATHS BY 58OHE 87TAMS 226
PRIMAL IDEALS AND ISOLATED COMPONENTS IN 56BRS 82TAMS PIIC
LATTICE OF SUBMODULES OF A MODULE OVER A 56FLR 81TAMS 342
NODAL 60SCR 94TAMS 310
F CHARACTERISTIC P. 58FLR 89TAMS 79
PROPERTIES OF PRIMARY 60CRL 94TAMS 75
ON SOME CLASSES OF 59FLG 90TAMS 323
A CLASS OF 62OSM 10JTAMS 483
WHITNEY CLASSES. 62BRN 104TAMS 374
ON A CLASS OF 62KSR 102TAMS 299
SOME IMBEDDING AND 62STD 103TAMS 403
ARY VALUE PROBLEMS FOR SYSTEMS OF ORDINARY, 60HRN 96TAMS 493
NONOSCILLATION THEOREMS FOR A CLASS OF 59MRE 93TAMS 30
HE STABLE INITIAL MANIFOLDS FOR 57LVN 95TAMS 357
ITERATION METHODS FOR 62SCR 104TAMS 179
ON A CLASS OF 60NHI 95TAMS 101
INTEGRATION AND 60GRS 94TAMS 404
LIC DIFFERENTIAL SYSTEMS. 60YEH 95TAMS 408
THE CHARACTERIZATION OF BEST 60RCE 96TAMS 322
ORTHONORMAL SETS WITH 61PRE 100TAMS 153
ORTHONORMAL SETS WITH 60PRE 95TAMS 256
56BSK 81TAMS 211
ENTIAL EQUATIONS. 59MRE 93TAMS 30
IFFERENTIELLE LE LONG DE CERTAINES COURBES 59GLR 93TAMS 169
DECOMPOSITION THEORY FOR 61CRY 99TAMS 246
CONTINUOUS MAPPINGS ONTO 57DGI 86TAMS 256

SINGULAR SELF-ADJOINT BOUNDARY VALUE PRO
MX.
NAKANO SPACES.
NATURAL NUMBERS.   CONSTRUCTIVE ANAL
NATURAL OPERATIONS ON DIFFERENTIAL FORMS.
N-CELL.
N-COMPLEX VARIABLES.
NECESSARY AND SUFFICIENT CONDITIONS FOR CARLSON'S THEOR
NEIGHBORHOOD OF AN INITIAL LINE.   A MAXI
NETWORKS.
NILPOTENT CENTRALIZERS.
NILPOTENT FUNDAMENTAL GROUPS.
NILPOTENT GROUPS.
N-MANIFOLDS.   SO
NODAL NONCOMMUTATIVE JORDAN ALGEBRAS AND SIMPLE LIE ALGEB
NOETHERIAN MATRIX RING.   PRIM
NOETHERIANOVERRINGS.
NOETHERIAN RINGS, II.
NOETHERIAN RINGS.
NON LINEAR PERTURBATIONS OF LINEAR SYSTEMS OF ORDINARY
NON BORNES DE L' ESPACE DE HILBERT. /L' EQUATION DU/D-
NONASSOCIATIVE RINGS.
NON-COMMUTATIVE FORMAL POWER SERIES. INTEFRATION OF PATH
NON-COMMUTATIVE POWER-ASSOCIATIVE ALGEBRAS.
NONCOMMUTATIVE RINGS.
NONCOMMUTATIVE RING.
NONCOMMUTATIVE JORDAN ALGEBRAS AND SIMPLE LIE ALGEBRAS O
NONCOMMUTATIVE RINGS.
NONCONTINUABLE ANALYTIC FUNCTIONS.
NONDEGENERATE SURFACES OF FINITE TOPOLOGICAL TYPE.
NON-DESARGUESIAN AFFINE PLANES.
NONEXISTENCE OF LOW DIMENSION RELATIONS BETWEEN STIEFEL
NONFLEXIBLE ALGEBRAS.
NONIMBEDDING THEOREMS FOR N-MANIFOLDS.
NONLINEAR, SECOND ORDER DIFFERENTIAL EQUATIONS. ON BOUND
NONLINEAR DIFFERENTIAL EQUATIONS.
NONLINEAR DIFFERENTIAL EQUATION. /ASYMPTOTIC BEHAVIOR OF T
NON-LINEAR PROBLEMS.
NONLINEAR SECOND-ORDER DIFFERENTIAL EQUATIONS.
NONLINEAR TRANSFORMATIONS IN HILBERT SPACE.
NONLINEAR VOLTERRA FUNCTIONAL EQUATIONS AND LINEAR PARABO
NONLINEAR TCHEBYCHEFF APPROXIMATIONS.
NON-NEGATIVE DERICHLET KERNELS. II.
NON-NEGATIVE DIRICHLET KERNELS.
NONOSCILLATION AND DISCONJUGACY IN THE COMPLEX DOMAIN.
NONOSCILLATION THEOREMS FOR A CLASS OF NONLINEAR DIFFER
NONRECTIFIABLES.   INTEGRATION D'UNE FORME D
NONSEMIMODULAR LATTICES
NON-SIMPLE SPACES.

FIGURE B1.

6. *Special Classification.* This would index published papers not only according to title, but according to specified aspects of their contents. For example, Dorothy Bernstein, presently at Brown, maintains an index on partial differential equations which lists for each review of a paper on partial differential equations the order, number of unknowns, number of independent variables, type (elliptical, hyperbolic, linear, etc.), and type of problem (Cauchy, Dirichlet, etc.).

This kind of index, as well as a Permuted Index might be a by-product of the automation of record keeping in *Mathematical Reviews.*

All such indexes should preferably be available in machine-readable form.

V. The problem of communication between mathematics and other fields is deserving of more effort than it now receives. There are already special meetings on applied mathematics and applications of mathematics. These meetings should be expanded and their existence should be better publicized among the users of mathematics. Next summer's meeting at Seattle on Relative Differential Geometry, Generalized Abelian Integrals, etc., is one sample. Another is a meeting that will take place at LSU this spring on C*-Algebras. About one third of the people attending this conference are expected to be physicists. The AMS conferences on applied mathematics are more examples. It probably would be wise to encourage such meetings not only in mathematical physics, but in mathematical economics and other applications.

A second channel for communicating mathematics to researchers in other fields is the writing of expository articles or expository texts. Such expository writing must be done at a level which is sufficiently unspecialized that it can be read by nonmathematicians. This might well have a corollary advantage of producing texts which will be of use to graduate students. We propose that the president of the AMS appoint a new committee to locate areas of mathematics which would be of maximum use to physicists (e.g., Lie groups), and to organize a writing panel of mathematicians and physicists to produce suitable expository material in this area. In the above sentence "physics" and "physicists" can be changed to "economics" and "economists" or to other disciplines at the discretion of the committee.

VI. More expository books are in order inside mathematics. These probably can be successfully commissioned and should be valuable to mathematicians in fields adjacent to that of the book, as well as to graduate students.

VII. In mathematics it seems clear that face-to-face communication is at least as important as any other one kind. A large amount of mathematical research typically is done by discussion among a small group of mathematicians of some tentative ideas proposed by one or more members of the group. Such a small group has much more knowledge of relevant results which have been recently proved than any one researcher working alone. Therefore, we commend the great efforts expended by various mathematical organizations in organizing meetings of all kinds, and we commend the government agencies which have made possible travel to such meetings and to smaller conferences. Up to now, the mathematical community has not taken kindly to the telephone as a substitute for personal meetings and it seems unlikely that adding a visual component to the telephone will make it much more acceptable.

In this context, too, some experimentation is in order. For example:

1. Devote half of some national meeting to a more closely planned, more detailed set of lectures; for example, a series of lectures whose texts are available beforehand, with discussion conducted by formally appointed persons who are acquainted with the text.

2. Schedule discussion-only sessions where papers are submitted and abstracts included in the program. The author would be available in a room for "argument." Several related papers could be scheduled in the same room with a discussion leader to chair the program. This is a possible substitute for 10-minute papers. It has been tried by the American Federation of Information Processing Societies.

3. Schedule a lecture on an important published paper by an expert in the field, not the author of the paper (in the style of the Fields Medal lecture at the International Congress).

4. Run a more extensive program in connection with the 20-minute invited papers. For example, there is to be a special session of 20-minute papers on Entire Functions at the Houston meeting. This will constitute a public presentation of some of the

reports and lectures given at the 1966 Summer Institute on Entire Functions. Furthermore, a second session on Entire Functions is being considered for the Houston meeting which would consist of a panel discussion with audience participation.

5. A meeting could include a set of lectures at a more expository level than present AMS lectures; for example, make them accessible to reasonably qualified graduate students. These lectures might be filmed or taped and distributed.

Small, specialized meetings seem to be very successful; more of them are being proposed (by CBMS). Perhaps the various kinds should be compared: summer-long teaching-and-research-microcosms (cf. Bowdoin) versus Gordon Conference types one or two weeks long; conferences which publish their proceedings versus those which do not, etc.

Are visiting lecturer programs worthwhile? CUPM and SIAM have some experience in this connection.

VIII.   To repeat, each of the preceding suggestions, if carried out, should be assessed after a suitable trial period. This assessment could be arrived at by a consensus (for example, no one doubts the great usefulness of small, select meetings suitably managed). However, for experiments with large meetings or with modes of publication some kind of formal survey will probably be in order. For example, tampering with sessions for 10-minute papers always brings an outcry at the AMS business meeting. Is this a real ground swell? A professional survey organization should be seriously considered for help in such matters, both in phrasing the questions to be asked and in evaluating the significance of the answers.

In any surveys that may be conducted, it will be important to tabulate separately the responses of different groups of mathematicians; for example, innovations should not be initiated on the basis of majority votes. For example, the following classes might be expected to respond in different ways.

1. A small group of first-rank mathematicians (to be selected by the committee, for example)

2. Productive mathematicians (five papers in the last five years, for example)

3. Mathematicians who are unproductive but not isolated

4. Mathematicians who are unproductive and isolated

5. Mathematicians in government and industry (should research labs be classed with universities?)

6. Physicists, economists, and other users of mathematics, productive in the sense of 2.

7. Editors or past editors of research journals and of technical series of advanced treatises

For some purposes it may also be desirable to classify mathematicians according to their field of interest. For example, it is possible that applied mathematics may have different needs. All this classification might best be done in advance of a survey, using *Mathematical Reviews* and other sources, rather than allowing each participant in the survey to classify himself.

IX. Finally, a bit of philosophy. We feel that our aim should be to channel the large masses of communication, not to limit them. Papers, lectures, etc. should be more carefully titled, abstracts should be used more and should be carefully written. This is partly a call for education of mathematicians in some of the simpler devices that can help buffer the avalanche.

We do not propose that the number of published papers should be restricted, because even if it can be demonstrated that the average paper has almost no readers, the writing, refereeing and publishing of the paper is of great value to the author. Besides making him visible to the mathematical community, presentation of his paper (in person or in print) exerts a certain influence that matures a fledgling mathematician (no research is complete until it is written down) and keeps older mathematicians alive; this seems to have some enlivening effect on the author's teaching and in his participation in other mathematical activities.

X. The present committee requests that it be discharged.

> P. R. Halmos
> Albert Madansky
> Alex Rosenberg
> J. Barkley Rosser
> J. D. Swift
> J. F. Traub
> A. S. Wightman
> D. Zelinsky, *Chairman*

Appendix C

The Role of the Private Foundations in the Support of Mathematics

A Report by L. H. Farinholt to the COSRIMS
Panel on Level and Forms of Support

GENERAL STATEMENT ABOUT FOUNDATIONS

In their support of mathematics as in their other grants, philanthropic foundations have consciously tried to stimulate new activities in preference to sustaining existing ones. Their general policy has been to provide the "seed money" which enables new enterprises to put down roots; once a "seedling" has proved its viability, the supporting foundation normally expects it to find sustenance elsewhere—from its parent institution, from public funds, and in some cases from industry. The "venture capital" which foundations provide is thus freed for work in other areas of need.

If, after a reasonable period of foundation nurture, the seedling shows no positive signs of becoming self-sustaining, the foundation usually will arrange to phase out its support and move on to more promising ventures. This risk of failure is inherent in most of the grants foundations make; in practice, a foundation naturally will try to assure itself in advance that the new enterprise has a reasonable chance of success.

Because foundations try to be creative rather than imitative in their grants, they take considerable pains not to become involved in programs that simply duplicate what is already being done with the support of government or other large benefactors. In this era of expanding federal support of science and education, it is no small

243

matter to remain abreast of burgeoning new federal programs, to say nothing of remaining ahead of them. But it appears unlikely that foundations will run out of things to do as long as they retain knowledgeable staff people and preserve their inherent flexibility in meeting new problems.

WHAT FOUNDATIONS HAVE DONE FOR MATHEMATICS

No private foundation has a separate division or program labeled "Mathematics." For reasons which the Committee will appreciate, the support of mathematics as a major undertaking has not been overwhelmingly attractive to even the most sophisticated of the large foundations. Warren Weaver has written: "The great private philanthropies have for the most part been rather cold to mathematics."*

Where mathematics has entered into foundation grants, it has usually appeared in projects to strengthen research and teaching in the sciences generally or to strengthen the scientific and technological capabilities of specific institutions. Mathematics also figures in grants where it is secondary to some other purpose, such as the construction of economic models or the mathematical analysis of medieval music.

For these reasons, any description of foundation grants "for mathematics" must be somewhat arbitrary and tentative. It must include grants that benefit "pure" mathematics, and it must not exclude those for applied mathematics; but it would seem reasonable to attempt to screen out those grants wherein mathematics is merely the tool of some other discipline. The standard adopted in this report (at Dr. Weaver's suggestion) is the inclusion of grants for work "by mathematicians in a mathematical setting." The time span covered is from the beginning of 1955 to 1966.

The total of grants for mathematics by the seven private foundations most directly interested in the discipline has been approximately $19,247,000 over the past 11 years. The Alfred P. Sloan Foundation has been responsible for over $10 million of this amount, the Ford Foundation and the Carnegie Corporation have each given more than $3 million, and the Rockefeller Foundation has contributed over $1 million. A more detailed description of each foundation's activities follows:

---

* Warren Weaver, *Mathematics and Philanthropy*, Alfred P. Sloan Foundation, 1965, p. 27.

Alfred P. Sloan Foundation ($10,422,078)

The Sloan Foundation's largest single contribution to mathematics has been its grants totaling $3,093,500 to the Courant Institute of Mathematical Sciences of New York University. Of this amount, $793,500 was a contribution to the program of the Institute and $2,300,000 was used in the construction of a new building which was named Warren Weaver Hall.

Other large grants were $1,265,700 for a laboratory of mathematics and physics at the California Institute of Technology; $1,000,000 for a mathematics center at Stanford University; and $500,000 for a mathematics center at Dartmouth College.

Grants to improve the teaching of mathematics have included $135,000 to Syracuse University for a project to upgrade selected high school teachers of mathematics, and contributions totaling $65,000 were made to the Mathematical Association of America in partial support of two summer institutes for college mathematics teachers. A grant of $60,000 helped the American Mathematical Society in moving its headquarters.

The foundation's Program for Basic Research in the Physical Sciences provides unrestrictive two-year research grants, with occasional renewals, to young faculty mathematicians, physicists, and chemists who show unusual promise. Under this program, since its inception in 1955, grants totaling $2,345,378 have been made to support the researches of 116 individual mathematicians.

The Sloan Foundation's support of mathematics continued unabated in 1965 and early 1966. A grant of $1,000,000 was made to Cornell University to help establish a new Department of Computer Science cutting across the boundaries of several Cornell colleges and professional schools. Brown University received $500,000 to help create stronger ties between mathematics and applied mathematics by strengthening faculties and facilities. A grant of $250,000 was made to help inaugurate a program in biomathematics at Sloan-Kettering Institute for Cancer Research and Cornell Medical College.

In the interest of mathematics education, the Sloan Foundation granted $100,000 to the Pacific Science Center Foundation to help establish a Regional Learning Center in Mathematics. A grant of $10,000 to the University of Cambridge, England, is supporting researches in the history of mathematics by Dr. Derek T. Whiteside.

Other grants by the Sloan Foundation have supported mathematics indirectly through the strengthening of certain engineering schools and of "science and mathematics" instruction in other colleges. Two large Funds for Basic Research in the Physical Sciences, one of $15,000,000 at Massachusetts Institute of Technology and another of $5,000,000 at California Institute of Technology, support some research work by mathematicians at those institutions. No effort has been made to include this indirect support in the Sloan Foundation's totals.

Ford Foundation ($3,326,000)

From 1958 to 1966, the Ford Foundation made twelve grants totaling $3,326,000 for mathematics, of which $1,000,000 was a contribution to the Courant Institute. Nearly all the rest was in support of educational projects such as curriculum improvement, development of new teaching materials, and seminars for grade school and high school mathematics teachers. The most recent grant, made in December 1965, was $155,000 to the Conference Board of the Mathematical Sciences, for a survey of the teaching and use of the mathematical sciences in the United States, in coordination with a related survey sponsored by the National Academy of Sciences.

Carnegie Corporation of New York ($3,181,000)

This foundation's interest also has been primarily in educational projects. In recent years, the Carnegie Corporation has granted $500,000 to Educational Services, Inc., for development of supplementary teaching materials in English and mathematics; $200,000 for the teaching of mathematics for engineering technicians in Milwaukee vocational and adult schools; $250,000 for curriculum-revision work at Webster College's Institute of Mathematics and Science; and $176,000 for the Mathematics Learning Center of the Pacific Science Center Foundation.

Rockefeller Foundation ($1,160,000)

Grants by the Rockefeller Foundation in mathematics have been made for educational purposes such as summer institutes for teachers and for larger projects which included mathematics. Among some forty-two grants thus involving mathematics, the figure of $1,160,000 is estimated to have gone for mathematics as such.

Louis W. and Maud Hill Family Foundation ($590,464)

This foundation in St. Paul, Minnesota, lists 29 grants since 1955 for projects in mathematics education, nearly all in the upper Midwest. It has supported experimental programs for gifted public school students, summer institutes for students and teachers, use of computers in colleges and universities, and comparative studies of mathematics education in this country and abroad.

John Simon Guggenheim Foundation ($356,000)

This foundation has awarded 82 fellowships totaling $356,000 to mathematicians in the past 11 years. Eight fellowships totaling $56,000 (included in the total) were granted to mathematicians in the past year.

Research Corporation ($211,500)

The Research Corporation since 1946 (a departure from the time span applied to other foundations in this report) has distributed $127,500 in grants to strengthen college mathematics departments; $16,000 in project grants; $28,000 for the Summer Research Institute of the Canadian Mathematical Congress, 1954–1956; $30,000 for a summer seminar of the Mathematical Association of America in 1964; and $10,000 to two mathematicians in its annual Research Corporation Award for 1963.

THE FUTURE OF FOUNDATION SUPPORT

For the future, it seems safe to say that foundations will continue to look for opportunities to do what other institutions cannot do or cannot do so well. Government support of science and technology, which seems to have reached a plateau, will continue to be a major factor in the thinking of foundations interested in those areas. The total amount of government support will be perhaps less important than the way in which it is distributed. Thus, if government support is to be spread more broadly on a geographical basis, foundations probably will be called upon to help remedy whatever untoward effects such a policy may have.

Most foundations, however, will continue to prefer to support innovative and experimental proposals, soundly conceived, rather than simply filling in the gaps left by other programs. In this function they have the advantage of flexibility and of relative—but not absolute—freedom from outside pressures. In the crossfire of conflicting demands made upon limited foundation resources, mathematics will have to make its case in competition with other and probably more dramatic appeals for support.

The pursuit of new knowledge has a strong appeal to many foundations. The problem for mathematics will be to demonstrate that new mathematical knowledge—and its application—is directly relevant to the social concerns that animate foundations.

Appendix D

The Support of Computer Use in Higher Education*

A Statement by E. A. Feigenbaum, Director, Stanford Computation Center

Automatic high-speed computing today [winter 1966] constitutes one of the nation's most important scientific and economic resources. Modern science and modern defense systems would be impossible without computers. Computation differs from other areas of "big science" in its immeasurably greater impact, now and in the future, on our social, economic, and educational processes and institutions. In the context of East–West competition, especially on national defense considerations, the state of computer science and technology was assessed at the White House level under President Kennedy.

Universities have played a major role in the development of this resource. Their ability to continue to do so is threatened by the application of certain auditing and accounting standards that in ordinary circumstances would be considered routine. At present

---

* The two memoranda included in this appendix were written at Stanford University in January or February 1966, in an attempt to explain a problem posed by a government auditing policy which greatly restricted the access of Stanford students to the Computation Center for instructional work. As of October 1967 the problem appears temporarily to be solved at Stanford University on an experimental basis. However, because the problem still has no permanent solution at most of our nation's universities, the memoranda are reproduced here as a statement of the problem. Some possible solutions are discussed elsewhere from a different point of view (see reference 38 of the main text).

249

there is no national policy toward computer *education*. No federal government program supports instructional uses of computers at universities. The standard auditing procedures (as relevant to the operation of a peanut factory as to a university computer center) have filled this policy vacuum. The result has been to generate an absurd situation in which an expensive computer facility sits idle and cannot be used to compute instructional jobs. The money to "buy time" to do these jobs is not available, even though the marginal cost of running the student jobs is virtually zero. To run these jobs would, literally speaking, not cost anybody anything. The facility is *at present* fully funded (primarily by recharges to federal government grants and contracts). It is the "logical" method of accounting for the time used that produces the absurd result.

What is the story behind this situation? When any growth process is geometric, the quantities involved grow very large very fast. Computer technologists have been observing and warning for years that the growth in demand for information processing done with computers has been a geometric growth. The general rule of thumb has been a doubling every two years. This average growth rate has been observed at all levels, from the federal government taken as a whole, down to the level of the small college or small business. Recently the pace has quickened somewhat, so that the period is now about 16 months. Even the world's largest manufacturer of computers has not been able to boost its production fast enough to keep up with the growth of demand. Policy makers and planners find it hard to keep pace with a geometric growth process, since normally the parameters of the management process grow slowly and are obviously under control. Thus the crisis caused by geometric growth sneaks up swiftly. In computing this has happened to the universities and to the government.

Consider the Stanford case. In 1953, a small Computation Facility was established, with a small budget. As demand for computing grew, the size of the facility grew to meet it, until in 1962 (and none too early) a Computation Center of the first magnitude was established and funded. A vigorous academic Computer Science program was begun, culminating in the establishment of a Computer Science Department in 1965 that now had 111 graduate students at the Master's and PhD degree levels. Vigorous educational efforts by the Computer Science faculty, and by the faculty of many other departments, were carried out. The result has been astonishing. It is estimated that currently one fourth of the Stanford community (faculty and students) are active computer users. The computer is used in virtually every phase of the university's work, in virtually every department and administrative function. In the Fall 1965 academic quarter over 1,000 students in 44 different courses used the computer in some part of their assigned homework. From September 1, 1965, to December 15, 1965, $150,000 worth of time for "unsponsored" graduate student and faculty research was allocated. The demand for "unsponsored" use during the 1965–1966 academic year has doubled since the 1964–1965 year—a factor of two in *one* year instead of the usual two. These numbers are the measure of Stanford's success in computer education and computer science. But the success has brought on a crisis, since under the present audit guidelines all the "unsponsored" use must be paid for at the supportable rate. The university's budget, with its slow growth from year to year, cannot absorb the impact of a geometric growth process, at least not immediately, because of a natural inertia in the budget. The crises in university computing, like a man's death, came "unexpected."

When computing was "small business" at universities, it received little attention from U.S. Government auditors. Because computing came to involve very large sums of money, and because of actual or presumed "irregularities" on the part of universities, the audit agencies reacted (some would say overreacted) by issuing tightly drawn audit guidelines, the effect of which will be to inhibit severely the future growth of computer education. A short statement on the audit policy by Courtney S. Jones, Assistant to the Controller, Stanford University, is appended.

Mr. Jones suggested one way out of the crisis—a change in the cost-accounting policy being applied. Another possibility is a direct congressional attack on the problem by enacting legislation establishing a policy toward, and appropriations for, educational uses of computers.

The absurdity of the present situation is hard to communicate in a short statement like this. It is best understood in the computer room at a major university like Stanford on a Sunday afternoon, after the run of jobs has been finished, and the computer and its operator sit idle. To use it for the students' jobs would cost nothing to anyone. The seconds, minutes, hours being wasted (translated into computer activity at 250,000 operations per second) are irrecoverable.

A Statement by Courtney S. Jones, Assistant to the Controller, Stanford University

Currently at Stanford for many hours a month the major computers are idle, and yet students and faculty who are eager to use these hours are turned away. It is reasonable to assume that a similar situation to a greater or lesser extent exists at most universities. The situation is the result of a shortage of funds for nonsponsored use of the computers in combination with the effect of the costing principles required by the government for allocating computer costs. The costing principles are set forth in the Bureau of the Budget Circular A21, paragraph J37. It is difficult, if not impossible, to attack the cost-accounting logic of the referenced paragraph that the government pay only that percentage of the costs which is its share based on hours of use. However, the result is that while the universities are providing computer services to government-sponsored research at rates significantly less than commercial rates, they are unable because of the costing mechanism to utilize without charge residual idle time for training students. Stanford, which is presently providing approximately $250,000 annually for nonsponsored users of the computers, cannot afford to increase the amount of these funds rapidly enough to meet the tremendous demand. Thus, computers are forced to be wastefully idle while this student and faculty demand for computer time goes unsatiated. An idle computer benefits no one, and when one considers that computers are probably idle to some extent in nearly all the universities in the nation, the amount of waste is immense. Clearly this waste is not in the national interest. It is also clear that a relatively simple remedy is at hand. The wastage could be eliminated by a government policy overruling the basic cost-accounting principle being applied, to the effect that the idle time could be used by otherwise unsponsored students and faculty. Such a policy properly implemented would result in no additional cost to the government. It would result in greater instructional and research benefits to the nation as the academic community utilized more fully the universities' computers.

Appendix E

PhD Origins of Mathematicians in Certain Categories

A Study Made for the COSRIMS Panel on New Centers

At the request of the COSRIMS Panel on New Centers, the American Mathematical Society compiled a list of the PhD origins of mathematicians in the categories shown in Table E-2. Mathematicians who received their doctorates before 1925 were not included in these tabulations. With few, if any, exceptions, those listed as foreign PhD's now teach in the United States.

The Panel next constructed the quality rating of PhD-granting mathematics departments in the United States shown in Table E-1. Quality ratings are given for the four successive decades (plus one year) in the period 1925–1965, the ratings for 1955–1965 being derived from Allan M. Cartter's study (see reference 32 of the main text) and for the decade 1925–1934 from Raymond Hughes' 1934 study for the American Council on Education (see reference 32 of the main text, page ix). The ratings for the two intervening decades are interpolations by the Panel.*

Using the ratings of Table E-1, CBMS Survey headquarters worked out Tables E-2 and E-3. Table E-2 utilized the American Mathematical Society compilation mentioned above. For Table E-3, the numbers of PhD degrees granted were taken from *Doctorate Production in United States Universities 1920–1962* by Lindsey Harmon and

---

* Within each category, the listing is alphabetical.

Table E-1   Leading United States Departments of Mathematics
Rated by Quality of Graduate Faculty

1925–1934	1935–1944	1945–1954	1955–1965
DISTINGUISHED	**DISTINGUISHED**	**DISTINGUISHED**	**DISTINGUISHED**
Chicago	Harvard	Chicago	California,
Harvard	Princeton	Harvard	Berkeley
Princeton		Princeton	Chicago
			Columbia
			Harvard
			MIT
			NYU
			Princeton
			Stanford
			Yale
STRONG	**STRONG**	**STRONG**	**STRONG**
California, Berkeley	California, Berkeley	California, Berkeley	Brandeis
Columbia	Caltech	Caltech	Brown
Cornell	Chicago	Columbia	Caltech
Illinois	Columbia	Cornell	Cornell
Johns Hopkins	Cornell	Illinois	Illinois
Michigan	Illinois	Johns Hopkins	Indiana
Minnesota	Johns Hopkins	Michigan	Johns Hopkins
Pennsylvania	Michigan	Minnesota	Michigan
Wisconsin	Minnesota	MIT	Minnesota
Yale	MIT	NYU	Northwestern
	Ohio State	Ohio State	Pennsylvania
	Pennsylvania	Pennsylvania	Purdue
	Texas	Stanford	UCLA
	Wisconsin	Texas	Virginia
	Yale	Wisconsin	Washington
		Yale	(Seattle)
			Wisconsin

Herbert Soldz of NAS-NRC and from the yearly lists published in
the *Notices of the American Mathematical Society*. The reader
should be warned that no canonical list of doctorates exists, and that
because of difficulties in classification and reporting, statistics from
different sources are in only fair agreement with one another.

TABLE E-2 PhD Origins of Mathematicians in Certain Categories

CATEGORY OF INDIVIDUAL	CLASSIFICATION OF PHD-GRANTING DEPARTMENT AT TIME INDIVIDUAL RECEIVED PHD (AMERICAN PHD'S SINCE 1925)			FOREIGN PHD'S SINCE 1925 (INCLUDES AMERICANS WHO OBTAINED PHD'S ABROAD)
	DISTINGUISHED	STRONG	OTHER	
I. Gave invited address at meetings of AMS in 1961–1966	34	23	9	19
II. Gave invited addresses at meetings of AMS in 1954–1960	40	17	13	21
III. Gave invited addresses at meetings of AMS in 1948–1953	23	19	9	25
IV. Gave invited addresses at meetings of AMS before 1948	24	19	10	21
V. Gave invited addresses (30 minutes or more) at International Congresses of Mathematics since World War II	36	13	6	37
VI. Members of National Academy of Sciences	14	4	3	15

TABLE E-3   Number and Percentage of Mathematical Science PhD Degrees Given by Distinguished and Strong Schools

	DISTINGUISHED		STRONG		OTHER		
TIME PERIOD	N	%	N	%	N	%	TOTAL
1925–1929	73	31	109	46	55	23	237
1930–1934	89	22	163	41	144	36	396
1935–1939	43	11	227	60	114	30	384
1940–1944	47	12	189	52	128	35	364
1945–1949	75	16	234	50	162	34	471
1950–1954	149	14	447	42	462	44	1058
1955–1959	425	34	356	29	485	38	1266
1960–1964	714	32	574	25	958	43	2246
1960	93	31	89	30	115	39	297
1961	136	36	81	22	157	42	374
1962	127	34	88	23	163	42	378
1963	179	32	159	28	229	40	567
1964	179	28	157	25	294	47	630
1965	200	29	186	27	303	44	689